MESCAL
AND
MECHANISMS OF HALLUCINATIONS

MESCAL
AND
MECHANISMS
OF
HALLUCINATIONS

HEINRICH KLÜVER

THE UNIVERSITY OF CHICAGO PRESS

Adapted from Stefan Szuman, *Kwartalnik psychologiczny*, 1930.

Library of Congress Catalog Card Number: 66-20593

THE UNIVERSITY OF CHICAGO PRESS, CHICAGO

Preface © 1966 by The University of Chicago

Il y a une espèce d'unité dans la variété qui me permettra de rédiger sans trop de peine cette monographie de l'ivresse....

CHARLES BAUDELAIRE

PREFACE

It is now 40 years since the late C. K. Ogden, the originator of Basic English, finding me in New York City in the throes of producing a manuscript entitled *Mescal: The 'Divine' Plant and Its Psychological Effects,* tried to convince me that readers in English-speaking countries would be most effectively and most speedily informed of my contribution if it were to appear in a monograph series published in connection with *Psyche—* a quarterly journal of general and applied psychology—which he edited at that time. His enthusiasm carried the day and as a result *Mescal* was published in London in 1928 as one of the "Psyche Miniatures" (6). Apparently it has been a collector's item for several decades; occasionally it is still listed in rare-book catalogues. In 1928 it was, as Macdonald Critchley pointed out in the Introduction, "the only monograph in English on the subject." It is fortunate indeed that the University of Chicago Press, cognizant of the interests and demands of an age of "psychochemistry," has decided to reissue this monograph (with a few minor corrections). I am particularly grateful to Dr. Critchley for allowing the reprinting of the admirable introduction he wrote for the 1928 book. The present volume, *Mescal and Mechanisms of Hallucinations,* contains, in addition to *Mescal,* another publication of mine, "Mechanisms of Hallucinations," to which many readers may not have easy access since it appeared in 1942 as a chapter in a volume published in honor of Lewis M. Terman (11). Grateful acknowledgement should be made to the McGraw-Hill Book Company for permission to reprint this chapter. Its inclusion in the present volume will, it is hoped, greatly enhance the value of the book since in "Mechanisms of Hallucinations" the analysis of mescaline-produced phenomena was carried out on a much broader basis than was possible in the 1928 *Mescal* monograph.

It has perhaps been forgotten that Ramón y Cajal, as he reports in his autobiography, hunted "in the flower garden of the gray matter . . . the mysterious butterflies of the soul," namely, nerve cells with elegant and delicate forms. The present-day hunt is chiefly concerned with catching these "butterflies" by means of chemistry or, more and more often, simply by means of drug-produced experiences. Nowadays the goal of Ramón y Cajal might even be considered a rather modest one, namely, that the beating of the wings of these butterflies would "some day—who knows?—clarify the secret of mental life." At the present time we seem to be in the habit of thinking in terms of goals that began to worry investigators, such as Havelock Ellis, even as early as 1902. After reporting his "study of a divine plant," that is, of mescal (4), he remarked that "it was inevitable that an attempt should be made to drag mescal into the already overcrowded field of therapeutical agents." Fortunately for his peace of mind, on examining the alleged therapeutic results obtained with mescal, he concluded that "there seems no excuse whatever for thrusting it into the pharmacopoeia." Surely, neither Havelock Ellis nor anybody else could have predicted at the turn of the century that the use of drugs would lead in 1965 to the publication of a book entitled *The Therapeutic Nightmare* (16) and that the President of the Society of Biological Psychiatry, Max Rinkel (the very man who introduced LSD-25 in this country), would feel called upon to discuss in his 1965 presidential address "problems connected with the use, misuse, and abuse of LSD in the United States." Furthermore, the age of psychochemistry has supplied us not only with an abundance of so-called "psychotherapeutic" drugs but also with "psychotomimetic" drugs which, in the opinion of certain psychiatrists, rarely, if ever, mimic the kind of "psychoses" they are used to; with "psychedelic" drugs, which, in the opinion of certain psychologists, rarely, if ever, produce manifestations of a "mind" they can recognize or have encountered in their professional endeavors; and with "hallucinogens" which rarely, if ever, produce hallucinations. It is apparent from such developments that the exploration of the "psycho" in psychochemistry—that is, the specification and analysis of the psychic functions involved—has not kept pace with advances along chemical lines. Since the conceptual tools for coping with so-called "subjective" aspects are often inadequate or entirely lacking, it is perhaps not surprising that many recent attempts at relating drug-produced experiences to schizophrenic or oneirophrenic experiences merely serve to recall Hoche's warning against "men who try to clear a turbid liquid by pouring it from one container into another" (5). It may of course be particularly difficult to eliminate "turbidity" and proceed to a development of the proper conceptual tools when not only an ever-increasing demand for psychotherapy appears as a symptom of the modern age (12), but also, as some observers insist, an ever-increasing demand for drug experiences. A deeper understanding of this situation would no doubt require a series of detailed historical and sociological studies. In the meantime, it is of some interest to point out that psychotherapists in Austria in pre-World War II days suggested discontinuing all psychotherapy for the sake of true psychotherapy (to concentrate all efforts on changing, for instance, the norms of penal codification), whereas psychotherapists of the post-World War II generation everywhere seem to insist on psychopharmaceuticals.

A historian will be aware of the fact that, aside from a psychology chiefly interested in obtaining information that can be used for influencing and controlling behavior, there has always been a psychology that is singularly free of such ambitions and content with determining the "structure" of the subjective world without reference to problems of great medical, social, or political significance. Contributors to such a psychology might argue that the present age is, first of all, in need of more monographs on heautoscopy, negative hallucinations, hypnagogic pseudohallucinations, "psychotoxic basic syndromes" (15), and numerous other problems of a fundamental nature (without reference to the therapy of mental disease). They might even argue for more books on normal perception (particularly in view of the fact that every "normal" perception may be said to have a "hallucinatory" component) or simply for more special treatises dealing with the perception of straight or curved lines (with special reference to the "visual sector" of the central nervous system as well as to a culturally articulated *Umwelt*). From such a standpoint, the investigations presented in *Mescal and Mechanisms of Hallucinations* appear as brave first attempts at describing and specifying the structure of our "subjective" world under a variety of conditions (the investigation of the effects produced by mescaline or other drugs being concerned with only one of these conditions). Joel Elkes would probably hold that such investigations are necessary and important on our road to recovery from the limitations of "objective" approaches. "In the psychological sciences," he pointed out 5 years ago, "we are only gradually recovering from the limitations of the so-called objective method" (3); yet such a recovery may not be easy since the determinations of the "subjective" world of man may involve us in difficulties fully as great as those encountered in attempting to specify or even understand the "subjective" world of animals. In a book dealing with brain functions in relation to psychic processes (17) Rohracher (Vienna) has stressed the enormous differences between the "personal worlds" of different humans and expressed the view that "everybody should know that there are other humans with whom he has nothing in common except the most primitive biological functions." It is certainly true that the "raw feels" (to use Tolman's expression) do not and cannot get across. However, as I have previously pointed out (7), there are no "red feels" or "moving feels": there are only red objects, moving objects, etc. *localized* in space and thus representing something to which actions and reactions of the most diverse kind are referable. It is for this reason that we are able to learn something about the phenomenal world in humans and animals (7, pp. 342–43).

Unfortunately, the existence of hopeful approaches to the subjective world of man (and even of animals) does not imply that they can be of much help at the present time in coping with the serious problems of mental disease and the pathology of behavior in general—problems which clearly cannot be solved or even formulated by "pure" psychologists. Waelsch has recently expressed the wish "that the time will never come when neurochemists will stop being biochemists" (23). One may also wish that the time will never come when pharmacopsychologists will stop being biopsychologists; it remains true though that there are problems which obviously demand the use of non-psychological tools, or at least the use of such tools in conjunction with psychological methods. Since I happen to be interested in some of these problems I could never reconcile myself to using "subjective" approaches only. At this point I should like, therefore, to mention briefly some (unpublished) experimental studies most of which were carried out 30 years ago.

In one series of experiments, normal as well as cortically injured monkeys (with occipital, parietal, temporal, or frontal extirpations) were trained to respond differentially to visual, auditory, or weight stimuli by using techniques previously described (7–10). The operated group of animals included monkeys in which the sensory roots of the trigeminal nerves had been cut (by Dr. P. C. Bucy) before bilateral removal of the somesthetic areas. It should be mentioned that the visual stimuli used in testing were different in brightness, color, size, and/or shape, and that, in presenting such differences, either light transmitted through opal glass or illuminated surfaces were used. In the mescalinized state, and under the particular experimental conditions employed, all differential reactions previously established through training remained intact, or were found to be only slightly disturbed when a comparison of the error curves in normal and mescalinized states of the animals was made. Despite the fact that in many of the experiments the doses injected were so large that the monkeys exhibited some of the symptoms characteristic of de Jong's "experimental catatonia," they aroused themselves again and again from their stuporous state to go through with the tests (although often refraining from eating the food they could obtain on performing a "correct" response). When normal and mescalinized monkeys were compared, not in terms of error curves, but in regard to the time relations in their reactions to the experimental stimuli, and particularly in regard to the time relations in the "comparison behavior" elicited by these stimuli, there appeared striking differences. In the test performances of the mescalinized animals there was an enormous slowing down of the motor reactions. It is of particular interest though that, despite the extreme slowness of motor reactions and despite the seemingly low level of alertness and wakefulness as indicated by general observation, the performance in tachistoscopic tests was not disturbed. (In these tests the animal was required to respond correctly to one of several visual stimuli exposed simultaneously for only a short time.) The experimental findings suggest, therefore, that "objective" observations, e.g., on aspects of motor behavior or on semistuporous and stuporous states in general, may be misleading when they serve as a basis for rash pronouncements on degrees of awareness in regard to sensory stimuli. In contrast to the information from general observations, the tachistoscopic tests indicated a relatively high level of sensory awareness and alertness since they demonstrated that the ability of registering and noticing stimuli of the external world and differentiating them quickly was not lost. Experiments of this kind bring home to us the great difficulties inherent in utilizing observations and measurements of motor behavior as a guide to the sensory world. "Objectively" visible and recordable evidence for "alertness" or "attention" may misguide us and even lead us to assume sensory concomitants or sensory determinants of behavior where none exist. Present-day investigators seem to be rarely concerned with a critical evaluation of the various factors entering into attempts at reconstructing the sensory world or special features of its organization from a limited set of "objective" observations; it is perhaps not surprising, therefore, that the step from "alertness" to "alertness centers" in the brain or from

"attention" to "attention centers" is nowadays a small one and
that "hallucinated" cats and monkeys have made their appearance in the literature. Since the difficulties I have in mind may
appear even in the analysis of seemingly "simple" forms of
behavior I should now like to refer to a second series of experiments.

In the second series of experiments the "oral syndrome" which
I first observed in mescalinized monkeys became the starting
point for a series of detailed studies. This syndrome is characterized by movements of the lips, tongue, and jaws, and often
associated with peculiar licking and chewing movements.
However, mescaline is not the only substance producing a
characteristic "oral syndrome"; such a syndrome or other oral
behaviors may be produced by a variety of other substances in
different animals. In studying the effects of 40 different substances in rats, rabbits, dogs, cats, and (normal and lobecto-
mized) monkeys of different species, I found that oral behaviors, or a syndrome exhibiting the same (or at least similar)
symptoms as the mescaline-produced syndrome, could be elicited by phenethylamine, 3,4-dimethoxyphenethylamine, 3,4-
diethoxyphenethylamine, 3,4-methylenedioxyphenethylamine,
α-methylphenethylamine, tyramine, ephedrine, cobefrine, ben-
zylamine, aniline, insulin, pentobarbital sodium, and apomor-
phine. The oral behaviors produced in different animal species
by various drugs undoubtedly involve heterogeneous mechanisms. For instance, in analyzing licking movements as observed
in monkeys, I found that there may be rhythmical tongue movements into the air, chop-licking, or licking of various objects,
including the floor or bars of the cage. In fact, it may be said
that under the influence of certain drugs you tend to lick your-
self while, under the influence of others, you lick the environment. In monkeys, the "oral syndrome" produced by mescaline
and a number of chemically related compounds never or only
rarely involved a licking of objects of the environment. The
appearance of this syndrome, however, was often associated
with peculiar "wiping" movements; more specifically, the
animal wiped, touched, and occasionally even scratched parts

of its head or face with one of its feet or hands and at times even seized and pulled at its lips. No doubt, observations of this kind have often formed the basis for assuming "hallucinated" monkeys. The wiping and the movements of touching, or almost touching, may suggest though that the "oral syndrome" with its characteristic movements of lips, tongue, and jaws is associated with, or even elicited by, somatosensory changes, particularly in the oral region. Human subjects, under the influence of mescaline, may report paresthesias and may even insist that saliva tastes like wine. Unfortunately, human observers when exhibiting a mescaline-produced "oral syndrome" may also report an absence of abnormal sensations or of other sensory changes and be unaware of the mouth movements they are performing. In other words, the observation of motor movements, whether in man or animals, may not permit reliable inferences as to the nature of the sensory concomitants of such movements or tell us whether the subject in question acts with reference to some sensory information or misinformation. Finally, in view of the fact that behavior manifestations are generally related to conditions in the internal as well as the external environment it deserves special mention that the mescaline-produced "oral syndrome" was found to be dependent not only on the quantity of the substance injected but also on factors operative in the external environment. For a monkey, the human "observer" often represents an emotion-arousing, or in many other ways significant, stimulus and his presence or absence may constitute one of the most effective behavioral determinants. In the experiments here briefly referred to I found that quantities of mescaline sufficient for producing a characteristic "oral syndrome" in the presence of an observer might not be sufficient in his absence. It seems, therefore, that under the particular conditions of these experiments an interaction between chemical and environmental factors was required for producing the syndrome. However, by sufficiently increasing the injected quantity the "oral syndrome" could be made to appear even in the absence of the human observer. In fact, mescaline injections in monkeys may produce a complex of symptoms, including oral behaviors, that resemble the "un-cinate" fits described by Hughlings Jackson at the end of the last century.

To return to the subject of "hallucinations" and related phenomena, it must be a disconcerting experience for those who happen to be interested in their genesis, behavior, and general significance to discover that the thousands of studies of mescaline, LSD-25, psilocybin, and other psychotoxic drugs undertaken in recent years have rarely provided an opportunity to investigate true hallucinations; nevertheless, these studies have been of great value since they have led to the realization, at least in certain quarters, that further progress in this field will depend on (1) a more thorough analysis of the biological factors associated with the appearance of hallucinations and (2) a more thorough search for the characteristics of subjective phenomena in general. Surely, the hallucination is only *one* of numerous subjective phenomena. At least a century of effort has gone into defining such phenomena, separating them and, in a series of ever-continuing attempts, isolating more and more of them. Perhaps the time has come to inquire into their *general* features and determine the characteristics that subjective phenomena have in common. To start with, it is worth stressing that variability and inconstancies appear to be the most constant feature of hallucinatory and other subjective phenomena. It would be even more challenging to consider, on the basis of a still broader psychological analysis, that instability, fluctuations, and oscillations are characteristics that various subjective phenomena, including hallucinations, share with olfactory, emotional, and sexual phenomena. Possibly the "neurobiology of normal and abnormal perception" might best be served by distinguishing a brain involved in fluctuations from one involved in "constancies." I have recently suggested that it is the temporal lobe, and especially the temporal rhinencephalon, which plays a dominant role in shifts, inconstancies, and fluctuations (13).

No doubt, it would be a task of forbidding magnitude to sketch even the broadest outlines of the work carried on along pharmacopsychological as well as neuro- and psychopharmacological lines during the last 40 years. However, in an age of organized research the reader may not find it too difficult to achieve at least a preliminary orientation by consulting, in addition to the current index and abstract journals and the volumes of the *Bibliography of Medical Reviews* (National Library of Medicine), the numerous transactions and proceedings of national and international conferences and symposia as well as the journals recently established for reporting developments in these fields. It should be noted in this connection that Baruk and Launay, when starting the *Annales Moreau de Tours* in Paris a few years ago, published in its first volume only psychopharmacological studies (1). The magnitude of the task of achieving a really thorough orientation in this field is probably best illustrated by the fact that a "bibliography of psychopharmacology" (2) should require fully 258 pages for listing publications for 5 years only (1952–57).

Since my early studies were focused on peyote or "mescal," I should be amiss at this point if I were not to call attention to the new enlarged edition of Weston La Barre's *The Peyote Cult* (14) as well as to some important papers by Richard Evans Schultes, whose scientific life has been so deeply concerned with "the widening panorama in medical botany" (18–22). Finally, I should like to recall with gratitude many stimulating and helpful discussions on biochemical and psychopharmacological problems with the late Gordon A. Alles during his frequent visits to my laboratory before and during the last war. I also wish to acknowledge the aid received from the National Institute of Mental Health, United States Public Health Service, for support of various researches (grant MH–01981) that in my opinion have proved to be of great importance for a better understanding of pharmacopsychological data.

HEINRICH KLÜVER

Culver Hall
University of Chicago
1966

REFERENCES

1   Baruk, H., & Launay, J. (eds.) Mémoires récents sur la psychopharmacologie. *Annales Moreau de Tours*, 1962, 1, pp. xv + 390.

2   Caldwell, A. E. Psychopharmaca. A bibliography of psychopharmacology, 1952–1957. *Publ. Health Service Publication No. 581*. Washington: U.S. Government Printing Office, 1958. Pp. iii + 258.

3   Elkes, J. Psychotropic drugs: observations on current views and future problems. *In* Brosin, H. W. (ed.). Lectures on experimental psychiatry. Pittsburgh: Univ. Pittsburgh Press, 1961. Pp. 65–114.

4   Ellis, H. Mescal: a study of a divine plant. *Popular Sci. Monthly*, 1902, 61, 52–71.

5   Hoche, A. Die Bedeutung der Symptomenkomplexe in der Psychiatrie. *Z. ges. Neurol. Psychiat.*, 1912, 12, 540–51.

6   Klüver, H. Mescal: The 'Divine' Plant and Its Psychological Effects. London: Kegan Paul, Trench, Trubner & Co., 1928. Pp. 111.

7   Klüver, H. Behavior mechanisms in monkeys. Chicago: Univ. of Chicago Press, 1933. Pp. xvii + 387. Also in Phoenix Science Series, Univ. of Chicago Press, 1961.

8   Klüver, H. A tachistoscopic device for work with sub-human primates. *J. Psychol.*, 1935, 1, 1–4.

9   Klüver, H. Use of vacuum tube amplification in establishing differential motor reactions. *J. Psychol.*, 1935, 1, 45–47.

10   Klüver, H. An auto-multi-stimulation reaction board for use with sub-human primates. *J. Psychol.*, 1935, 1, 123–27.

11   Klüver, H. Mechanisms of hallucinations. *In* McNemar, Q., & Merrill, M. A. (eds.). Studies in personality. New York: McGraw-Hill Book Co., 1942. Pp. 175–207.

12   Klüver, H. Psychology at the beginning of World War II: meditations on the impending dismemberment of psychology written in 1942. *J. Psychol.*, 1949, **28**, 383–410.

13   Klüver, H. Neurobiology of normal and abnormal perception. *In* Hoch, P. H., & Zubin, J. (eds.). Psychopathology of perception. Proc. 53d Ann. Meeting Amer. Psychopathol. Assoc., 1963. New York: Grune & Stratton, 1965. Pp. 1–40.

14   La Barre, W. The peyote cult. Hamden, Conn.: Shoe String Press, 1964. New enlarged ed. Pp. 260.

15   Leuner, H. Die experimentelle Psychose. Ihre Psychopharmakologie, Phänomenologie und Dynamik in Beziehung zur Person. *Monogr. Gesamtgeb. Neurol. Psychiat.*, 1962, **95**, pp. x + 275.

16   Mintz, M. The therapeutic nightmare. Boston: Houghton Mifflin Co., 1965. Pp. xxviii + 591.

17   Rohracher, H. Die Arbeitsweise des Gehirns und die psychischen Vorgänge. München: Barth, 1953. Pp. 173.

18   Schultes, R. E. Peyote and plants used in the peyote ceremony. *Botanical Museum Leaflets Harvard Univ.*, 1937, **4**, 129–52.

19   Schultes, R. E. Peyote *(Lophophora Williamsii)* and plants confused with it. *Botanical Museum Leaflets Harvard Univ.*, 1937, **5**, 61–88.

20   Schultes, R. E. Tapping our heritage of ethnobotanical lore. *Economic Botany*, 1960, **14**, 257–62.

21   Schultes, R. E. The widening panorama in medical botany. *Rhodora*, 1963, **65**, 97–120.

22   Schultes, R. E. Ein halbes Jahrhundert Ethnobotanik amerikanischer Halluzinogene. *Planta Medica*, 1965, **13**, 125–57.

23   Waelsch, H. Biochemical interpretations of neurophysiological vectors. *Perspect. Biol. Med.*, 1965, **9**, 165–86.

CONTENTS

PART I

MESCAL: THE 'DIVINE' PLANT AND ITS PSYCHOLOGICAL EFFECTS

INTRODUCTION

The cult of the Echinocactus Williamsii (peyotl; mescal) and the remarkable train of phenomena which follow its ingestion have constituted a most fascinating study for many years. Despite the singularity of the symptoms of mescal intoxication, the drug had remained but little known until the treatises of Rouhier and Beringer in recent years made it familiar to us. This present volume, the work of Dr. Klüver, is, however, the only monograph in English on the subject. Within its pages the author has dealt with the broad aspect of the subject; he has written of the rituals and ceremonies with which the native devotés have surrounded this plant, which indeed they have exalted to divine rank. Klüver also deals shortly with the pharmacological aspect of the crude drug and its constituent alkaloids. The size of the volume, however, has precluded any detailed account of these particular aspects, and the author has wisely devoted the bulk of the monograph to the physiological and (more particularly) the psychological standpoints of mescal intoxication and chronic mescalism. This work is therefore something more than a general discussion of mescal in all its features; it is a most valuable contribution to the psychological aspect of the extraordinary hallucinosis which is so characteristically produced by this drug. Within these pages we read for the first time a most careful and detailed analysis of the visual and other phenomena which comprise the *ivresse peyotline,* and we are furthermore given an intimate study of the associated personality changes.

Fortunately rare in this country, mescal addiction is common in the New World, among the Indians of Mexico and even of some of the southern of the United States—particularly Texas and New Mexico. As Klüver points out, there is evidence that increased facilities of transport have in recent years disseminated the mescal cult far beyond the original confines. In this country the employment of mescal has been almost entirely restricted to the researches of a few experimental pharmacologists and psychologists, such as Dixon and Havelock Ellis.

Mescal is unique among drugs in that its main action is a stimulant of the visual and visuo-psychic areas of the cortex. Hence the characteristic effects of ingestion take the form of visual hallucinations of varying complexity and distortions or perversions of visual perception—all of which are most ably described by Klüver. In some instances also, other sensory activities share in the excitation, and alterations in the function of the special senses or bodily feelings may be present.

For the purpose of description one may conveniently divide the visual phenomena of mescalism into: (1) visual hallucinations; (2) alterations in the vividness of visual imagery; and (3) apparent change in the aspect or behaviour of real objects.

Each of these manifestations is analysed by Klüver and he deals first with the nature and characters of the hallucinations. He describes how various "form-constants" frequently recur—spirals, cones, lattice-work and so on; the factors of colour and illumination are considered. Questions of localization within the visual field, of motility, of symmetry, of dimension and of plurality are investigated. A tantalizing sense of incompleteness often characterizes these visions, and Klüver discusses fully this interesting aspect, which he speaks of as the "presque vu" phenomenon.

Changes in the intensity of visual imagery are of interest in mescal intoxication and the author takes up the question of the influence of thought upon the development and nature of the hallucinations.

The appearance and behaviour of surrounding objects may seem markedly altered during the acute stages of mescalism. Thus Klüver describes megalopsia or micropsia; illusions of movement; the endowment of excessive speed to objects actually in motion; the vivid enhancement of detail.

Rarer and less characteristic are the changes in other sense fields—olfactory, auditory or gustatory. Thus we may find hyper- or hypo- sensitivity in these respects, perverted reactions, or actual hallucinations. Of especial interest are the not infrequent occurrence of synaesthesiae in mescal states, whereby excitation of one sense organ by actual stimuli evokes a train of phenomena pertaining to another sense organ. These resulting features may comprise either a particularly well defined mental image or else actual illusory or hallucinatory concepts. Thus we may encounter audito-visual, audito-tactual, visuo-tactual, tactuo-visual and other types of synaesthesia. The first is perhaps the commonest and constitutes one of the varieties of the so-called *audition colorée*. Putt, for example, found during a state of mescal intoxication that each audible stroke of a pendulum produced an "explosion of colour." Prentiss and Morgan discovered that the beat of a drum had the power of increasing the beauty and variety of the visions. One of Rouhier's subjects stated that the sound of the low notes of a piano produced an hallucination of violet, while high notes gave rise to rose and white. The harmonies of a musical composition evoked grandiose architectural visions—"a basilic court with statues." Dixon also may be quoted in this connection: "the effect of the sound of the piano was most curious and delightful, the whole air being filled with music, each note of which seemed to arrange around itself a medley of other notes which appeared to me to be surrounded by a halo of colour pulsating to the music." Many other examples could be cited to illustrate this association between sounds and vision. In this respect one is reminded of the similar synaesthetic effect of *cannabis indica*—so well described by Gautier[1] and by Baudelaire.[2]

---

[1] "Mon ouïe était prodigueusement dévélopée. J'entendais le bruit des couleurs. Des sons verts, longs, bleus, jaunes m'arrivaient par ondes parfaitement distinctes. Chaque objet effleuré rendait une note d'harmonie ou d'harpe éolienne."

[2] " . . . Les transpositions d'idées les plus inexplicables ont lieu. Les sons ont une couleur, les couleurs ont une musique."—*Les Paradis Artificiels.*

Synaesthesiae between colour and taste have also been recorded: thus Havelock Ellis described how, on one occasion, a colour (green) took on a sweetish and somewhat metallic taste in his mouth. Blue, in turn, had a taste resembling phosphorus. In respect of these special sense linkages, mescalism resembles the bizarre and barely describable aurae and confusional states which may occur in migraine and epilepsy, whereby stimuli from one sense organ are perceived and described in terms of other sense channels, as though short-circuiting processes were at work along unusual transcortical pathways.

From the visions themselves, Klüver passes to an investigation of the so-called "mescal psychoses" and the reaction of the individual himself towards his hallucinosis. As we might expect, these latter are indeed variable. All manner of emotional response may occur—depression, indifference, interest or euphoria. With larger doses, profound changes in orientation in time and space may occur and dominate the picture; thus Fernberger, who took as much as 39 grains of mescal, had few hallucinatory experiences but became grossly disorientated in all spheres. Mixed somatopsychic aberrations, ideas of transposition of personality, haptic illusions of infinite variety are among the more fascinating of the diverse aspects of mescal intoxication.

So much for the present status of mescalism; the importance of the drug in the psychological research of tomorrow is admirably sketched by Klüver. It is obvious that in the possession of an agent such as mescal—with so selective an action—we have an instrument which may prove of the greatest value. Possibilities of its employment in research along neurological and ophthalmological fields can only be guessed at, and a use in the investigation of cortical and sub-cortical activity is most suggestive. The therapeutic aspect of the problem is still unknown. Some fifteen years ago Maloney reported success from the use of mescal in cases of optic atrophy, but the lack of supporting evidence suggests a non-fulfilment of early promise.

Klüver's contribution to the literature of mescal will do much to bring into greater prominence the properties and possibilities of this most extraordinary drug. It is to be hoped that English investigations will become familiarized with this plant and be encouraged to employ it in the many suggestive and therapeutic, psychological and neurological avenues of research which lie open.

MACDONALD CRITCHLEY

London,
    August, 1928.

1

"MESCAL BUTTONS"

> "As the Semitic mind could conceive, and the Aryan mind could accept the Semitic conception, that deity may be incarnated in an animal body—that is, a human body—so to the American Indian mind it seems just as reasonable to conceive that deity may dwell in a plant body."
>
> M. R. GILMORE

The importance of mescal for psychological research cannot be questioned. We shall deal here with the psychological effects of this drug, with special reference to the unusual visual experiences which characteristically result from its use.

"Mescal buttons" or "mescal beans" are the dried tops cut from several species of the cactus Lophophorus (*Anhalonium*), particularly from *L. Williamsii* and *L. Lewinii*. The drug has different names among the Indians using it: e.g. "hikori" or "hikuli" among the Tarahumaris; "huatari" among the Cora Indians; "seni" among the Kiowas; and "wokowi" among the Comanches. "Peyote" is the general commercial term being derived from the Aztec "peyotl" which is the Nahuatl word for "cocoon." The tops sliced off from the small fleshy spineless cactus bear in the center a mass of whitish hairs in which the small flowers are partly concealed. When dried, these tops become hard and brittle, and shrink to button-shaped discs, one or two inches broad and from an eighth to a quarter of an inch thick. These mushroom-like discs, coming especially from the plants growing in northern Mexico and on both sides of the

Rio Grande, are spread among the Indians of the United States under the misleading name "mescal buttons." This name is misleading because "mescal" may be confused with one of the most common intoxicants in Mexico, the distilled liquor mescal. It would be better to use the word "peyotl" for the drug, a term preferable from the etymological point of view. Nevertheless, we shall use "mescal," since this term has been employed in almost all scientific English publications on the subject.

The botany and chemistry of the drug are still a matter of dispute. Whether or not *L. Lewinii* is a variety instead of a distinct species is one of the unsettled questions. Safford maintains that the surface of *L. Lewinii* has usually thirteen ribs, separated by strongly sinuous grooves, but that sometimes there are twelve, or even as few as nine ribs; the typical *L. Williamsii* is supposed to have eight ribs, sometimes as many as ten, separated by straight, or almost straight, lines. On the basis of these observations, Safford inclines to the view that the different types are connected by intermediate forms and that they cannot, therefore, be specifically distinct. All of them may be classified under *L. Williamsii*. Here we note that the specimen which we received as *L. Williamsii* from the National Museum, Washington, D.C., through the courtesy of Dr. J. N. Rose, has ten ribs. In general, the botanical investigations concerning the specificity of *L. Lewinii* have not led to any definite results.

The same uncertainty exists with regard to the chemistry of the drug. L. Lewin was probably the first who attempted a chemical analysis of mescal. Heffter continued this work and reached the conclusion that morphologically similar plants may differ radically in their chemical constituents. But it seems that there is still much work to be done before this conclusion will be generally accepted. Heffter called the alkaloids found in *L. Lewinii* mescaline, anhalonine, anhalonidine, and lophophorine. Especially mescaline, $C_{11}H_{17}NO_3$, has been used in experimental studies on the psychological effects of the drug. Instead of pursuing further the discussion of the botanical and chemical questions, we may here refer the reader to Rouhier's *Le peyotl* for orientation.

According to Mooney, "a detailed account of the mythology,

history and sacred ritual in connection with the mescal would fill a volume." Here a few pages must suffice for the principal historical and ethnographical facts.

In many Indian tribes mescal has become the center of elaborate religious ceremonies. After 1890 the ceremonial use of the drug spread among the Indians as far north as the Sioux and Chippewa and west to the Ute. Shonle believes that in the centuries prior to 1890 "peyote spread at most to only five or six tribes north of the Rio Grande," and that since 1890 it has been carried to some thirty additional tribes, a result which is partly explainable by the fact that postal service and railway travel make the transportation of mescal buttons easy. For many centuries mescal ceremonies were only found among those tribes whose wanderings brought them through or near the Rio Grande Valley and the adjacent regions, through the "peyote country." The rapid spread of the "peyote cult" beginning before 1900 represents many features of special interest to the anthropologist. The ceremonies of various tribes differ in characteristic ways. A number of variations are due to the introduction of Christianity. We shall cite here Shonle's description of the ceremonies among the Tarahumare Indians:

"The peyote ceremony of the Tarahumare is preluded by a ceremonial pilgrimage to the peyote country for the purpose of securing the plants. The chosen company before starting is purified with copal incense. Although several days are consumed in the journey to the peyote country the men eat nothing until they arrive. . . .

"The first act upon arriving among the peyote is to erect a cross before which peyote are placed that they may tell where other peyote grow. Raw peyote plants are then eaten and further work is postponed until the following day, after the intoxication has worn off. Peyote are then gathered with a certain ritual and the company returns home, usually having spent several weeks or a month on the journey. Their return is hailed with songs and a sacrificial feast.

"The peyote ceremony is held in connection with the other tribal dances, but not as an integral part of them. A special patio is cleared of rubbish and swept; logs are brought for the fire and arranged to lie in an east and west direction. Two or three women are appointed as assistants to the shaman who is to have charge of the ceremony; they grind the peyote on the metate before the ceremony, taking care not to lose any of the liquid or the water in which the metate is afterward washed. The dirty brown mixture which results is drunk at the dance.

"When evening comes, the shaman seats himself west of the fire with a male assistant on either side and the women assistants to the north of the fire. A cross is placed to the east of the fire. On a symbol of the world a peyote plant is placed and covered with a hollow gourd which is used by the shaman as a resonator for his rasping stick.

"The order of the ceremony consists of singing by the shaman to the accompaniment of the rasping which continues through the night; offering of incense to the cross by assistants who kneel and cross themselves; dancing by the male assistants who wear white blankets and carry rattles of deer-hoofs (this dance follows a line contrary to the motion of the sun and occupies the space between the fire and the cross with a later extension to include the fire); dancing by the women assistants; drinking of the peyote by all who are in attendance. The only variation in the procedure comes at daybreak when the people gather near the cross for the healing service. This is accomplished not by the direct use of the peyote, which is, nevertheless, thought to have curative power, but by rasping against the person's head, the slight dust from the rasping being thought efficacious in producing health. After healing the people, the shaman rasps toward the rising sun to waft the peyote spirit home. The ceremony ends with this service and is followed by a feast."

Mooney reports that he saw a twelve year old boy eating six mescal buttons and that twelve to twenty is a common number for adults. He refers to an Indian who took even as many as ninety buttons.

In this connection we may call attention to the fact that many experimenters who took the drug themselves chewed and swallowed either the dry mescal buttons, usually three to seven, or ground the buttons to powder and took the powder. Others used a decoction or injected one or several of the alkaloids subcutaneously. Thus Knauer and Maloney administered 0.15 to 0.20 gm. of the sulfate of mescaline subcutaneously; Beringer injected as much as 0.6 gm. In the References will be found mention of the original publications which describe the conditions under which the different experimenters have obtained their results. The literature shows that the conditions under which experimental data on the effect of mescal have been secured are not always comparable in the different experiments. But in spite of differences in the amount and the chemical constituents of the dose as well as in age, sex and general condition, etc., of the subjects, it is possible to give a summary of *typical* mescal effects. We will consider those phenomena which are typical of the psychological effects of the drug; we are not concerned here with a discussion of the physiological effects. The results concerning the physiological action of mescal have been summarized by Rouhier. It has been pointed out that mydriasis is about the only constant symptom found in all subjects and that nausea is reported by a great number of cases. But with regard to other symptoms, no general results have been obtained.

2

MESCAL VISIONS

"Qu'éprouve-t-on? que voit-on? des choses merveilleuses,
n'est-ce pas? des spectacles extraordinaires? Est-ce bien
beau? et bien terrible? et bien dangereux?"

BAUDELAIRE, *Les Paradis Artificiels*

It has been known for a long time that "visions" are the most
characteristic symptom induced by mescal. But it is only recently that a sufficient number of self-observations have been
made to enable us to analyze with any certainty the optical
effects of the drug. The data available do not warrant any general conclusions concerning the causative factors of these phenomena; as to the "why" we must rely on future experimental
work. Our analysis is only concerned with the "how" of the
optical effects. Of special importance in this respect are the
studies by Beringer, Rouhier, Knauer and Maloney. Valuable
contributions have been made by Dixon, Havelock Ellis, Fernberger, Guttmann, W. Jaensch, Weir Mitchell, Serko, Mayer-
Gross and Stein, Prentiss and Morgan. Knauer and Maloney
experimenting on themselves and on physicians in Kraepelin's
clinic made altogether twenty-three experiments. Rouhier refers
to five observations, and Beringer to "about 60" trials. Beringer,
who worked in the Psychiatric Clinic in Heidelberg, used
chiefly physicians and medical students as subjects. Six of his
subjects were women. The 32 observations published by Beringer in 1927 are of outstanding importance. Our analysis has
principally to rely on these records and on the results of the

few experimental studies available. Before entering into a discussion, it will be well to illustrate certain characteristics of mescal visions as found in the records of different experimenters.

Knauer and Maloney, upon injecting 0.2 gm. of the sulfate of mescaline into the subcutaneous tissue of the forearm, obtained four hours after the injection the following report from one of their subjects: "Immediately before my eyes are a vast number of rings, apparently made of extremely fine steel wire, all constantly rotating in the direction of the hands of a clock; these circles are concentrically arranged, the innermost being infinitely small, almost point like, the outermost being about a meter and a half in diameter. The spaces between the wires seem brighter than the wires themselves. Now the wires shine like dim silver in parts. Now a beautiful light violet tint has developed in them. As I watch, the center seems to recede into the depth of the room, leaving the periphery stationary, till the whole assumes the form of a deep funnel of wire rings. The light, which was irregularly distributed among the circles, has receded with the center into the apex of the funnel. The center is gradually returning, and, passing the position when all the rings are in the same vertical plane, continues to advance, till a cone forms with its apex toward me." In the following the subject describes "beautiful crimsons, purples, violets, blues and greens" quickly succeeding one another. The background of this "gorgeous color panorama was first like faintly illuminated ground glass; it is now a silvery tint, and is deepening into a yellow like pure gold. . . . On pressing upon my eyes, the whole picture seemed to materialize." The wires became "more solid, more real and quite distinct from the background." "The wires are now flattening into bands or ribbons, with a suggestion of transverse striation, and colored a gorgeous ultramarine blue, which passes in places into an intense sea green. These bands move rhythmically, in a wavy upward direction, suggesting a slow endless procession of small mosaics, ascending the wall in single files. The whole picture has suddenly receded, the center much more than the sides, and now in a moment, high above me, is a dome of the most beautiful mosaics, a vision of all that is most gorgeous and harmonious in color. The prevailing tint is blue, but the multitude of shades, each of such wonderful individuality, make me feel that hitherto I have been totally ignorant of what the word color really means. The color is intensely beautiful, rich, deep, deep, deep, wonderfully deep blue. It is like the blue of the mosque of Omar in Jerusalem. . . . The dome has absolutely no discernible pattern. But circles are now developing upon it; the circles are becoming sharp and elongated . . . now they are rhomboids; now oblongs; and now all sorts of curious angles are forming; and mathematical figures are chasing one another wildly across the roof. The colors are changing rapidly—from blue green to black, to brown—passing successively through an infinite variety of transitional shades. . . ." Six hours after the injection, the subject sees "a beautiful palace, filled with rare tapestries, pictures, and Louis Quinze furniture. . . ." In the rooms ladies appear "without motion . . . as a series of portraits. . . ." Twenty hours after the injection there are outlines "suggesting crocodiles, lizards and other reptiles . . . they arouse absolutely no sensation of fear." There are "visions of human intestines, of sections of abdomens, and sections of the pregnant uterus. . . ."

As a second example of mescal visions we quote from the report of Weir Mitchell who, "at 12 noon of a busy morning," took 1½ drachm of an extract "of which each drachm represented one mescal button." One hour hereafter, little over a drachm was taken and at about four o'clock half an ounce of this extract in three doses. Soon Mitchell found himself "deliciously at languid ease." At 5:40 he noticed a number of star points and fragments of stained glass with closed eyes. He went into a dark room: "The display which for an enchanted two hours followed was such as I find it hopeless to describe in language which shall convey to others the beauty and splendour of what I saw." "Stars . . . delicate floating films of colour . . . then an abrupt rush of countless points of white light swept across the field of view, as if the unseen millions of the Milky Way were to flow a sparkling river before the eye . . . zigzag lines of very bright colours . . . the wonderful loveliness of swelling clouds of more vivid colours gone before I could name them. . . ." Then, for the first time, "definite objects associated with colours" appeared. "A white spear of grey stone grew up to huge height, and became a tall, richly finished Gothic tower of very elaborate and definite design, with many rather worn statues standing in the doorways or on stone brackets. As I gazed every projecting angle, cornice, and even the face of the stones at their joinings were by degrees covered or hung with clusters of what seemed to be huge precious stones, but uncut, some being more like masses of transparent fruit. These were green, purple, red, and orange; never clear yellow and never blue. All seemed to possess an interior light, and to give the faintest idea of the perfectly satisfying intensity and purity of these gorgeous colour-fruits is quite beyond my power. All the colours I have ever beheld are dull as compared to these. As I looked, and it lasted long, the tower became of a fine mouse hue, and everywhere the vast pendant masses of emerald green, ruby reds, and orange began to drip a slow rain of colours. . . . After an endless display of less beautiful marvels I saw that which deeply impressed me. An edge of a huge cliff seemed to project over a gulf of unseen depth. My viewless enchanter set on the brink a huge bird claw of stone. Above, from the stem or leg, hung a fragment of some stuff. This began to unroll and float out to a distance which seemed to me to represent Time as well as immensity of Space. Here were miles of rippled purples, half transparent, and of ineffable beauty. Now and then soft golden clouds floated from these folds, or a great shimmer went over the whole of the rolling purples, and things, like green birds, fell from it, fluttering down into the gulf below. Next, I saw clusters of stones hanging in masses from the claw toes, as it seemed to me miles of them, down far below into the under-world of the black gulf. This was the most distinct of my visions." In his last vision, Mitchell saw the beach of Newport with its rolling waves as "liquid splendours huge and threatening, of wonderfully pure green, or red or deep purple, once only deep orange, and with no trace of foam. These water hills of colour broke on the beach with myriads of lights of the same tint as the wave." Again, the author considers it totally impossible to find words to describe these colors. "They still linger visibly in my memory, and left the feeling that I had seen among them colours unknown to my experience."

William James received a supply of mescal buttons from Mitchell. He tried the drug and reports on the results in a letter to Henry James: "I took one bud three days ago, was violently sick for 24 hours, and had no other symptom whatever except that and the *Katzenjammer* the following day. I will take the visions on trust!" Even Mitchell writes "These shows are expensive. . . . The experience, however, was worth one such headache and indigestion, but was not worth a second."

We refer now to our personal observation to demonstrate some other aspects of mescal visions. 23 gm. of the powdered buttons were taken in doses of 13 and 10 gm. Half an hour after taking the second dose vomiting occurred. Soon hereafter phenomena of the following kind could be observed with closed eyes: "Clouds from left to right through optical field. Tail of a pheasant (in center of field) turns into bright yellow star; star into sparks. Moving scintillating screw; 'hundreds' of screws. A sequence of rapidly changing objects in agreeable colors. A rotating wheel (diameter about 1 cm.) in the center of a silvery ground. Suddenly in the wheel a picture of God as represented in old Christian paintings.—Intention to see a homogeneous dark field of vision: red and green shoes appear. Most phenomena much nearer than reading distance.—The upper part of the body of a man, with a pale face but red cheeks, rising slowly from below. The face is unknown to me.—While I am thinking of a friend (visual memory-image) the head of an Indian appears.—Beads in different colors. Colors always changing: red to violet, green to bright gray, etc. Colors so bright that I doubt that the eyes are closed.—Yellow mass like saltwater taffy pierced by two teeth (about 6 cm. in length).—Silvery water pouring downward, suddenly flowing upward.—Landscape as on Japanese pictures: a picture rather than a real landscape.— Sparks having the appearance of exploding shells turn into

strange flowers which remind me of poppies in California.—
(Eyes open): streaks of green and violet on the wall. Then a
drawing of a head changing into a mushroom (both of natural
size). Then a skeleton (natural size) in lateral view turned
about 30° to the left. Head and legs are lacking. Try to convince
myself that there are only shadows on the wall, but still see the
skeleton (as in X-ray).—(Eyes closed). Soft deep darkness with
moving wheels and stars in extremely pleasant colors.—Nuns in
silver dresses (about 3 cm. height) quickly disappearing.—
Collection of bluish ink-bottles with labels.—Red, brownish and
violet threads running together in center.—Autumn leaves turn-
ing into mescal buttons.—Different forms emitting intense
greenish light.—Forms in different colors; contours often dark.—
Strange animal (length perhaps 10 cm.) rapidly turns into
arabesques.—Gold rain falling vertically. On stationary background rotating jewels revolving around a center. Then, with a
certain jerk, absence of all motion.—Regular and irregular
forms in iridescent colors reminding me of radiolaria, sea urchins and shells, etc., in symmetrical or asymmetrical arrangement.—Shells illuminated from within radiating in different
colors, moving towards the right, turned about 45° towards the
right and somewhat towards me. A little piece in every shell is
broken out.—Slow majestic movements along differently shaped
curves simultaneously with 'mad' movements.—Feeling there is
'motion *per se*.'—Man in greenish velvet (height about 7-8 cm.)
jumping into deep chasm.—Strange animal turns into a piece of
wood in horizontal position."

We shall now analyze the visions produced by mescal to determine the typical characteristics of these phenomena. It is
hoped that the excerpts cited above will illustrate some of the
points now under consideration.

At the very beginning, our search for typical effects seems
to meet serious difficulties. On the one hand, the investigators
emphasize that the phenomena defy all description. On the
other hand, the phenomena reported present such striking differences in appearance that it seems more adequate to stress
the diversity of these phenomena than the "common elements."

As regards the first point, we find—although, as Havelock Ellis puts it, "the chief character of the visions is their indescribableness"—that a comparison of those aspects of the visions which have actually been described, yields positive results. Furthermore, we note that, descriptively, "indescribableness" refers in most cases to the transitoriness and to certain qualitatively new aspects of the phenomena not previously experienced by the subject in such a way. As regards the second point, it is clear that the extremely variable optical effects found in some cases have to be kept in mind when it comes to statements about "typical" effects. This variability can, as the data show, be only partly explained by reference to differences in the chemical properties of the alkaloids employed. Even if kind of extract, dose and method of administering are kept constant, the symptomatic picture varies in certain respects from person to person and in the same person from time to time. In Serko's case for example, in the first experiment the chief symptoms were visions, in the second "haptic hallucinations" and in the third "associative disturbances." Though the visions which are hardly ever absent in the drugged state may in various cases strikingly differ in appearance, it seems safe to predict that future work will hardly add new characteristic variants to those which are known at present, at least not for adults of the white race.

In discussing the typical features of these phenomena we should call attention first to a certain characteristic *sequence* of the visions. Knauer and Maloney consider the following sequence "characteristic of practically all the poisonings": wavy lines; mosaics; carpets; floral designs; ornaments; wood-carving; windmills; monuments; mausoleums; panoramic landscapes; statuesque men and animals; finally scenes picturing episodes in a connected manner. Rouhier attempts to establish four types of mescal visions. He recognizes, however, that they do not correspond to successive stages of the *"ivresse divine."* His belief is that in general these types are "intimately mixed," but that one of these types dominates the others during the mescal state. Geometric figures and kaleidoscopically changing forms are considered characteristic of the first type. Sometimes these forms remind the observer of objects seen in his past life. H. Ellis writes: "The visions never resembled familiar objects; they were extremely definite, but yet always novel; they were constantly approaching, and yet constantly eluding, the semblance of known things. I would see thick, glorious fields of jewels, solitary or clustered, sometimes brilliant and sparkling, sometimes with a dull rich glow. Then they would spring up into flowerlike shapes beneath my gaze, and then seem to turn into gorgeous butterfly forms or endless folds of glistening, iridescent, fibrous wings of wonderful insects. . . ." According to Rouhier the second type of visions is represented by familiar objects, landscapes, faces, etc. whereas the visions of the third type, which are supposed to be especially characteristic of mescal, cannot be traced back to events of the past. Monstrous forms, fabulous landscapes, etc., appear. Mitchell's visions are cited for illustration. The phenomena of the fourth type are said to have remarkable similarity with those produced by hashish. It seems to us that any scheme which, in a detailed manner, assigns different kinds of visions to successive stages of the mescal state must be viewed as extremely arbitrary. The only thing that is typical with regard to sequence is that very elementary visions are followed by visions of a more complex character. In general, the phenomena observed first are seen by pressing upon the eyeballs. Thereafter, visions appear with closed eyes without such stimulation. Then, they may be seen with open eyes in the dark room and even in broad daylight. It is to be noted, however, that in some cases pressure on the eyeballs is entirely ineffective.

The initial phase of the visions as observed with closed eyes may be illustrated by some excerpts from the records: "Clouds from left to right through optical field" (14[1]); "the appearance of visions with closed eyes was very gradual. At first there was merely a vague play of light and shade which suggested pictures, but never made them" (1); "when I had the eyes closed, it became brighter and brighter around me . . . this brightness which possessed depth . . . in-

---

[1] The numbers in parentheses refer to the numbers in the References.

creased more and more and was finally so impressive that, in spite of my being in the dark room and knowing that my eyes were closed, my critical attitude surrendered to this sensuous vividness and I opened my eyes expecting as a matter of fact to sit in a bright room. I found that the brightness impression lasted. I turned around to find the source of light. It seemed very strange that it was bright but that I could not see anything" (13).

Such elementary brightness and color visions are succeeded by forms and form combinations for which frequently the same descriptive terms are used by different observers. We hear for example, that the forms and designs are in general of "the same character as the images of the kaleidoscope, symmetrical groupings of spiked objects . . . glorious fields of jewels . . . living arabesques . . ." (1). We hear of "a steel veil the meshes of which are constantly changing in size and form . . . beads in different colors . . . red, brownish and violet threads running together in center . . . gold rain falling vertically . . . regular and irregular forms in iridescent colors" resembling radiolaria, sea urchins, and shells (14); "transparent oriental rugs, but infinitely small" seen for example on the surface of the soup at lunch time or with closed eyes (13); "plastic spherical filigreed *objects d'art* similar to Haeckel's radiolaria . . ."; "wallpaper designs . . ."; "countless rugs . . . with such magnificent hues and such singular brilliancy that I cannot even imagine them now . . ."; "the design was not an ordinary chessboard design any more, but the chessboard motive repeated itself, the design became increasingly delicate, the details assumed the character of ornaments . . ."; "cobweb-like figures or concentric circles and squares . . ."; "in the four squares of a coordinate system, I saw moving bands . . . finally in the center there remained a female shape as if cut out of ivory . . ."; "the pyramid of the tower of a Gothic dome . . . architectural forms, buttresses, rosettes, leafwork, fretwork, and circular patterns . . ."; modern cubistic patterns . . ."; "gammadia forms from the points of which radiate innumerable lines in the forms of screws and spirals, in flashes and calm curves . . ."; "a kaleidoscopic play of ornaments, patterns, crystals, and prisms which creates the impression of a never-ending uniformity" (13).

So far the analysis of the records published has yielded a number of forms and form elements which must be considered typical for mescal visions. No matter how strong the inter- and intra-individual differences may be, the records are remarkably uniform as to the appearance of the above described forms and configurations. We may call them *form-constants,* implying that a certain number of them appear in almost all mescal visions and that many "atypical" visions are upon close examination nothing but variations of these form-constants.

Some of these constants require a special consideration on account of their possible bearing on the origin of the visionary phenomena. One of these form-constants, for example, is always referred to by terms such as *grating, lattice, fretwork, filigree, honeycomb,* or *chessboard design.* To quote different observers: "Soon there grew up an extremely beautiful architecture before my eyes. Hexagonal small honeycombs hung down from the ceiling . . ."; "stripes which formed a sort of fretwork . . ."; "somewhat later I saw shadow-like gratings . . ."; "incessant play of filigreed colors . . ."; "in the face of B, I saw a lattice of yellow-greenish horizontal stripes . . ."; "ornamental fretwork" (13). Here we mention the fact that one of Beringer's subjects, a physician, sees constantly a fretwork difficult to describe which becomes of central importance in the psychotic state induced by mescal: "I am fretwork; I hear what I am seeing; I think what I am smelling; everything is fretwork . . . I am music, I am climbing in music; I am a touching fretwork; everything is the same." The large number of variations of the fretwork-constant must be kept in mind when it comes to relating these visionary fretwork structures to observations on similar structures reported upon in the field of sensory physiology, e.g. by König and Helmholtz.

Closely related to the form-constant just discussed is the *cobweb* figure. The following excerpts taken from the records of different observers illustrate this phenomenon: "Colored threads running together in a revolving center, the whole simi-

lar to a cobweb" (14); "immense areas over which gigantic cobwebs were spread . . ."; "cobweb-like forms . . ." (13). In one
case the subject was looking at an acacia standing before the
window: "Very much to my surprise the leaves of a small branch
suddenly appeared in an ornamental pattern as though joined
in a circular design having the form of about a cobweb. I looked
at other branches, and, looking at them, all leaves assumed the
same lattice-like arrangement" (13).

A second form-constant which deserves special mention is
designated by terms as *tunnel, funnel, alley, cone* or *vessel.* To
illustrate: "Sometimes I seemed to be gazing into a vast hollow
revolving vessel, on whose polished concave mother-of-pearl
surface the hues were swiftly changing" (1); "the field of vision
is similar to the interior of a cone the vertex of which is lying
in the center of the field directly before the eyes (or vice
versa)" (14); "vision of a tunnel in copper-brown color . . . lines
seem to converge in the infinite"; "a large black corridor seen
in extremely deep perspective" (15); "upon pressure on the
closed eyes I saw first an alley in very deep perspective"; "deep
beautiful perspectives . . . growing into the infinite . . ."; "in
deep perspective a suite of oriental rooms"; "extending away
from me a long narrow corridor . . . often looking into cupolas
which widen more and more . . . the cupola became increasingly
deeper, more funnel-shaped, narrower"; "I was standing in a
very long and wide tunnel"; "long narrow funnels . . . the ends
of which appear in the distance as brilliant points . . . their walls
and the perspective effects are in most cases formed by small
parallel lines . . ."; "a large cylindrical hall"; "the designs occupied the wall of a colossal cone"; "the pyramid changes into a
luminous cone" (13). The large number of what may be called
architectural variations of the funnel-shape is of special interest.

A third important form-constant is the *spiral.* "Upon rhythmical whistling there appears a brown spiral, a wide band, revolving madly around its vertical axis. The band spiral opens
and closes as a concertina according to the rhythm of the
whistling whereby bright light falls through the intermediate
spaces"; "a procession, coming from the lower right, moved

slowly in spiral turns to the upper left"; "wire-like thin black lines in curves and spirals drawn out" (13). In this connection we shall refer to the remarkable experiences of Serko. In his description of "haptic hallucinations" he mentions that he had the sensation as though one of his legs had spiral form. "In the diffusely illuminated visual field a luminous spiral forms itself through the active movement of a stripe. This quickly rotating spiral is moving back and forth in the field. At the same time . . . one of my legs assumes spiral form . . . The luminous spiral and the haptic spiral blend psychologically, that is to say, the same spiral which is optically hallucinated is also haptically experienced. In an hallucinatory way the leg blends haptically with the luminous spiral. . . ." A physician, a subject of Beringer, reports: "Before me I see the lower part of my body from the hips down as a large green varnished object which has about the shape of a truncated cone with spiral windings." The same subject experiences the sounds of a concertina coagulating in the spiral windings of the body.

From the discussion of the most characteristic form-constants we shall turn to an examination of some of the visual properties of the phenomena. As regards *color tone* one is struck by the large number of variants in this respect. In general, mescal does not produce a preponderance of certain colors to the exclusion of others. At present it seems impossible to state a general rule concerning hues and their sequence in mescal visions. Referring to our own observation, the result was: "All spectral colors can be observed. There is no indication that certain colors occur more frequently than others. Sometimes approximately complementary colors appear simultaneously or successively." Some observers report that "red" and "green" seem to dominate the initial phases of the visions and that "blue" and "yellow" appear later. Other reports indicate that some color tones do not appear at all, as e.g. "blue" or "red and green." In some cases, black, red, brown, violet or blue dominates the picture. Again, it is reported that the colors succeeding each other are contrast colors. In one report we find the statement: "With open eyes one sees pairs of colors, green-red, blue-yellow or brown-red, floating up and down as balls. These colors may assume the shape of a kitten, a bird or a dainty ladies' shoe." It is apparent that any attempt at formulating a general law becomes futile.

The *brightness* of many visions is so intense as to call forth a blinding sensation. "I was able to press but a short time on my eyes since the brightness of the colored configurations arising hereafter increased so excessively that I was blinded and felt pain . . ." (13); "a luminous pyramid, about 1 m. long; the vertex is a glaring white; concentrating on it, a blinding sensation results" (13). Frequent reference is made to "lightnings," "comets" and "explosions." "Suddenly very intense bright light as if produced by an exploding shrapnel (apparently a few cm. from the eyes). Almost simultaneously jerky movement of hand to make sure whether blinders are on" (14).

Some of the above quoted descriptions of mescal visions show clearly that an unusual *saturation* is likewise one of their outstanding features. It seems to be especially this characteristic which leads to the often repeated statement that it is impossible to find words to describe mescal colors. But, in addition, there are many other phenomenal aspects of these colors for which psychology is about to develop technical terms. So far there is a deplorable lack of such terms. What we have in mind here is best illustrated by the observation of Havelock Ellis who was not only impressed "by the brilliance, delicacy, and variety of the colors, but even more by their lovely and various textures—fibrous, woven, polished, glowing, dull, veined, semitransparent." For a more adequate appreciation of the phenomenology of mescal colors a large number of similar terms could be added from other reports. Here we shall add only the remark of one observer which shows that the "texture" of some colors is apparently not worth the *Katzenjammer*: "My visual sense is enriched, but the colors lack 'color'; they are nothing but . . . 'shines' " (13).

We turn to what the subjects call the *illumination* in and of the field in which the phenomena appear. It is of great theoretical interest that not only the brightness value of the different parts in the visual field may change but that frequently reference is made to an "illumination" of the visionary figures. One of Beringer's subjects reports: "The illumination of the picture seemed to come from an unknown, invisible source of light and was moving now and then, in the form of a stripe, from the left to the right and vice versa, but never from top to bottom . . . ." From other subjects we hear: "Legs of spiders in the upper right of the visual field; somehow, they seemed to be illuminated from behind, the light coming from afar . . ."; "a face half human, half animal . . . the eyes and the mouth are extremely bright as if the whole were illuminated by an electric bulb . . ." (13). Rouhier's subjects also refer to invisible sources of light which illuminate the visionary objects.

As regards the distribution of the colors, forms or configurations in the field of vision, most observers emphasize the *symmetry* of the phenomena. The geometric center of the field is often the center around which various patterns are grouped; it may assume a certain distinctness as to brightness, color or movement. This tendency to symmetry becomes apparent also in the different shapes and form elements themselves. On account of this symmetry most subjects are particularly struck by any kind of *asymmetry* which may appear: "There were often a certain incomplete tendency to symmetry . . ." (1); "tapestries with pearl and gold embroideries, pottery, mosaic work, in most cases symmetrical, rarely asymmetrical . . ."; "all designs came out of an invisible hole which was situated near the right boundary of the visual field . . ."; "vision of irregular fragments . . . these fragments appear in the upper visual field to the left" (13). A woman, one of Beringer's subjects, had the feeling that the right half of her face was displaced downwardly. "At the same time there was a veil of faint rainbow colors from top to bottom before my right eye."

With regard to the *localization* of the phenomena the statements of different observers differ widely. In case the eyes are closed, the phenomena are, at least very often during the beginning of the visions, localized at the distance of the visual gray. As soon as the field is filled up with visionary designs and objects, difficulties in localizing arise very often. The same uncertainty as to position in space may exist when the eyes are open. Sometimes the phenomena are definitely localized on the walls, on the floor or wherever the subject happens to look. Some subjects feel that they cannot make any definite statement as to position, at least not with respect to some of the phenomena. There are even persons who report that the phenomena are "in the eyes" or "in the head." Or: "It is not possible to localize them definitely in space; they seem to me rather near, but floating indefinitely in the air . . ." (13). This shows that the phenomena frequently defy, in G. E. Müller's terminology, an exact egocentric localization; the attempt at localizing them entoptically or even intracranially is undoubtedly often nothing but an expression of the uncertainty of the subjects. Such uncertainty does apparently not exist with regard to relative localization, with respect to the position of objects to each other. In general the visions do not move with the eyes. Sometimes a visionary object seems even to have a definite position in perceived space. "I look in a different direction. After a short time there appear pale, sad looking human faces . . . I look back in the first direction and, frightened for a moment, see the head at the same place" (13).

With respect to *dimensionality* we note that visionary forms may be of two or three dimensions. In some cases, the surfaces of objects are described as "reliefs" the objects as "extremely plastic figures." Again and again the observers compare the designs and forms with artistic products of the Orient. To illustrate: "Then I saw halls and passages very plastically . . . I was able to observe various details; I noticed for instance several times that two vaults were separated by a very sharp edge. On one side of the edge it was extraordinarily bright, on the other side it was shaded . . . I estimated the distance between me and the nearest point of the passage to be $1\frac{1}{2}$–2 m. . . . I saw the hallucinated room very distinctly and I knew the distance of the different points. I believed that it was possible to seize some of the objects. . . . One time I saw a man in natural size in the background. . . . He performed certain movements but first I

could not see what he did . . . I could see the face of this man
so clearly that I would recognize him for instance on a photo-
graph. The man stood in the most distant part of the room at a
distance of about 8–10 m."; "the plastic, distinctly visible oriental room . . . I did not find any difference between seeing it
and the viewing of objectively existent surroundings . . ."; "the
meadow was perhaps at a distance of 100 paces . . . in the foreground, at a distance of 8 m., I saw huge wooden snails, a horse-
whip for children with a red ribbon and similar things . . . I saw
every grass blade; it was clear to me that every blade had to
stand just where it did, to bend itself just the way it did and to
cast such a small shadow . . ." (13). The last observation is made
with open eyes in the dark room. Very frequently, the subjects
point out that there are different backgrounds behind each
other. Some of them may disappear, others may remain stationary. Occasionally, there is a sudden transition from blurred
drawings to distinct perspective. In general, constant change
seems to be more typical of the initial stages of the mescal
"intoxication." The accounts refer to "furious succession" of
colors, to "mad" movements and rotations and to "motion *per
se*." At the climax of the intoxication, however, visionary forms,
such as human and animal faces, monsters, and architectural
details can be viewed comfortably. The following is observed
with open eyes in twilight: "Then there appears a colorful pig
in the upper corner of the room as a large suspended marionette, the long snout which alternately shortens and protrudes
is distinctly visible . . . behind the ears of the pig is a wooden
figure with red trousers whose night-cap is indistinctly continuous with the wire of the marionette . . . while looking at this
figure the pale face of a girl with a red shawl . . . appears . . . I
see her very distinctly . . ." (13). Certain visions are of such
solidity that they do not disappear or become indistinct upon
the appearance of objective light. "The eyes open, the hall—
and vault—pictures dominated in the dark room. A cigarette
placed into them did not interfere with the observation, but was
seen as a foreign light in the hallucinated room. One of the
columns, for example, was always behind the cigarette which

was moved back and forth; a column, actually standing in the room, was about one meter to the right from the hallucinated column when the light (of the cigarette) appeared" (13).

In considering the *size* of the visionary objects we find that they vary from "gigantic" domes to "Lilliputian" figures. Personally with closed eyes we did not see any form the dimensions of which exceeded 10 cm. The squares seen in one of our designs were 2 × 2 cm.; their size did not seem to change upon opening the eyes. Many observers report macropsia and micropsia. There may be a dysmorphopsia of figures with which the subject is familiar on the basis of past experience. Changes in the apparent size of the same figure also occur.

Here we may raise the question whether or not it is possible to *influence visions* by "thinking" or to cause the appearance of new visionary objects by imaginal processes. Most subjects apparently do not manage, in any of the phases of the intoxication, to influence the visions; some succeed to a certain extent, but only a few are able to "see" objects upon thinking of them intently. It is to be noted that most observers state that visions and visual memory-images exist independently. The investigation of Knauer and Maloney brought out that visual images could be "controlled, changed and recalled as in normal life, but not with the same facility." But this does not seem to hold in all cases since along with an increase in the vividness of memory-images some individuals discover a greater facility in "controlling" them. On the other hand, it may even be entirely impossible to call up certain visual images. Some of the facts just mentioned are illustrated in the following: "The wish to 'see' the buildings . . . in Brussels could not be realized. I noticed, however, that my imaginative faculties were qualitatively and quantitatively increased" (13); after a picture had been placed on a background and then removed "I tried to see the picture with open eyes. In no case was I successful; only visionary phenomena covered the ground" (14); the subject while watching the vision of a danseuse on a stage attempted "to picture a shoe. He repeated to himself all the separate parts of a shoe, and endeavored by concentration to bring up an hallucinatory image of a shoe. The danseuse continued to dance undisturbed for some time, and then suddenly and unexpectedly there appeared a gigantic misshapen shoe, seemingly moulded in plaster, and colored green" (3); "Dr. B. named different persons and pictures which I was to imagine. Soon, thereafter, they appeared to stand in perceived space, well-defined and plastic; some of them appeared on the projection background in the most minute details; some persons as e.g. my parents seemed to be in natural size before me . . ." (13); another subject tries to "see" roses and notices "after about half a minute scintillating dark red points, very difficult to fixate, in addition green spots; the whole a sort of wallpaper design as one would expect to find in the room of a flapper; the red spots grow, the central parts seem to assume the shape of leaves; they become similar to roses, the whole not very distinct"; "it is certain that I can imagine any object I please, in a more concrete way than usual, but I am not under the impression that I really see it . . ."; "I tried to force myself to imagine Michelangelo's 'Evening' and 'Morning' but I did not succeed" (13).

Of considerable interest is the fact that sometimes a visionary object appears first singly and, thereafter, as multiple. Such instances of *polyopia* in visions seem to be rather frequent. They represent an interesting parallel to the multiple seeing of real objects with open eyes while in the mescal state and to the polyopia in eidetic and basedoid persons. "A small wooden face appears, it has the form of a small apple; then there comes a small yellow face; suddenly there are three, four faces in one row; above it new rows appear . . ."; "there are animals in frantic motion, I see a crow and a black cat racing on, and behind them five, six animals of the same kind . . ."; "suddenly a little man is standing there changing continually in appearance, sometimes he has a beard, sometimes not, the covering of his head is also changing . . . now the little men increase again in number until there is a whole line of them . . . one of them twirls his moustache, and at once all of them twirl their moustaches with a tremendous speed . . ."; "I saw a huge black organ with bright metal pipes, at the top they became increasingly smaller. At first the organ was stationary; then out of the upper pipes there developed smaller and smaller pipes moving upwards continually followed by new pipes. The motion was rather slow, and I was able to observe the rise of pipes very distinctly . . ." (13); "moving scintillating screw; 'hundreds' of screws . . ." (14); "open the eyes for a few seconds, look at the experimenter and close them: positive after-image of the face of the experimenter. His hair turns into hair of a cat, his eyes get a bright yellowish color. Then the head of a cat (natural size); hereafter the whole field filled with yellow eyes" (14).

In this connection we should like to refer to an instance of multiple vision observed by the Indian "Crashing Thunder" whose autobiography has been edited by Paul Radin. "It was now late at night. I had eaten a lot of peyote and felt rather tired . . . As I looked again I saw a flag. I looked more carefully and saw the house full of flags. They had the most beautiful marks on them."

In discussing the chief characteristics of mescal visions attention should be called to some hitherto insufficiently analyzed visual "experiences" in the mescal state. The first of these experiences which we propose to call the *presque vu*—experience arises in the following way: the phenomena and events in the visual field point in a certain direction; that means, they suggest an end which is not quite reached, or they lack the proper completion; they do not—to use a *Gestalt* psychological term—call forth a "closure"—experience. A form, a movement, a pattern, etc. is almost complete, but since it never becomes entirely completed, a very characteristic *presque vu*—experience arises. The contour of a figure is almost complete, but it never is quite; a movement or a form element suggests a connection between two shapes or patterns, but this connection is never quite established; a pattern lacks a certain element which is "outside" of the field of vision, this element is almost in view but the final and satisfying completion never takes place due to the "extracampine" location of the missing element. In such cases the optical basis for the *presque vu*—experience is obvious; the fact that during a "mescal psychosis" a special, or even "cosmic," meaning is attached to this visual experience is a different matter. In some cases the subject does not know the exact visual basis for his *presque vu*—experience: "In center bright light as coming from an electric bulb. Bulb seems to be incomplete. Then brilliant bluish form running through the field; seems to be incomplete in a certain way. In both cases unable to state what is lacking and how the impression of incompleteness arises . . ." (14).

We call the second experience the *dual system*—experience. Sometimes the visual phenomena and events observed fall into two groups. The hues, shapes, designs and movements, etc. in one group seem radically different from those of the other group. Thus the observer has the feeling of viewing two "systems" or even two "antagonistic" systems as he may refer to them e.g. as "solar" or "polar" systems. Frantic motion may be typical of one system while slow majestic movements are characteristic of the other one. In psychotic states these two systems the differences of which are merely differences in visual properties may gain "cosmic significance." One of Beringer's subjects reports: "The moment came nearer when the two polar systems would vibrate in tune, when their centers would be united for the formation of an enormous structure. Then I should be able to see everything, no limits would exist for my experience and understanding. A disgusting trismus destroyed this moment of maximal tension. . . . Again and again they came, again the strong mental tension, the desire to see a solution, and again, in the most critical moment, the painful trismus. . . . Again forms appeared that fought with each other. In concentric circles, from within Gothic forms, from without Romanesque forms. Rejoicing more and more, becoming bolder and bolder, the pointed Gothic forms penetrated the Romanesque arches and pressed them together. And again, shortly before the decision, the trismus."

3

CHANGES IN
DIFFERENT
SENSE FIELDS

"Il est temps de laisser de côté toute cette jonglerie. . . ."
BAUDELAIRE

From the analysis of visions we shall turn to an examination of the changes brought about by mescal in the different sense fields. Especially the changes in *visual sensation* and *perception* deserve a detailed consideration. Most investigators have been more interested in the vision-producing effects of mescal than in the sensory changes caused by the drug. But an analysis of only the visions would leave our account of the optical effects incomplete. Not only would it be incomplete but at the same time we should not arrive at a proper understanding of the way the visual world appears to the subjects. The visionary world and the objective world, observed at the same time with open eyes, are phenomenally not as discrepant as one would expect. Even if visions are not seen with open eyes, the *Sehdinge* of the objective world may undergo certain characteristic changes. Only a few investigators have attempted to determine the nature of these changes experimentally.

In examining the results, one is struck by the great variability in the changes produced. These perceptual changes may differ from case to case, from one intoxication to the other, and in different stages of the same intoxication. With respect to colors, there are frequently changes in brightness and saturation, especially noticeable in peripheral vision. Sometimes the colors are brighter and more deeply saturated than usual; sometimes certain hues objectively present seem to disappear, "everything appears green-blue or green-red, I see nothing but red and green in the world, and I am looking for blue and yellow." It may even happen that "the whole room appears uniformly gray and colorless." Very often the objects seem to lose their solidity, especially upon looking at them for a while. In other words, the colors change from "surface" colors (Oberflächenfarben) in the sense of Katz to "film" colors (Flächenfarben). In some cases, however, the objects appear more solid than ever, the surface colors are more sharply defined, there is an increase in brightness. Occasionally, the objects are surrounded by halos of one or several colors. In some cases, it is difficult to say whether there is merely a change in the perception of the object or whether we have what may be called a "visionary transformation" of the object. The following two observations are made by a physician: "I notice that brown stripes are coming gradually out of my fingers. Moving my hands, the stripes move just like burnt soft cords; it is possible to bring the hand with the cords near to my face and move it back thus putting the hand into the cords . . ."; "suddenly the contours of the objects are surrounded by a light blue, hazy halo, this is especially noticeable on the hair of a colleague . . ." (13). Rapid color changes on a real object may occur: "Dr. L. gleamed alternately in violet, yellow, and white light."

Small differences in the hue and brightness of real objects are often noticed. Whether or not mescal actually produces a change in differential sensitivity cannot be answered at present. The experimental investigation of this problem is confronted with a number of serious difficulties which will not be discussed here at length; but it is a fact that most observers report a hypersensitivity concerning colors. It is not clear whether this implies a lowering of the thresholds or is indicative of changes in so-called "optical attention." Furthermore we must not overlook that there are reports indicating visual hyposensitivity during the mescal state.

An enhancement of contrast phenomena seems to be the rule. Very pronounced simultaneous contrast is found; the contours of the objects become sharp and well-defined. Of special theoretical importance are the data on the behavior of after-images. Referring to our own observation we found that, while fixating a stimulus object, e.g. a paper—square, in order to produce an after-image, the background, which consisted of one of Hering's gray papers, was most of the time covered with ever-changing designs. The stimulus object was also covered with varying forms and colors. Now and then, the phenomena on the background appeared in the complementary color of the square which we were fixating. Sometimes we could observe the normal marginal contrast, but it was more pronounced than usual. The hues of the after-images obtained did not differ from those seen under normal conditions. In some instances, the visions prevented the appearance of after-images entirely; in most cases a sharply outlined normal after-image appeared for a while. Then the after-image became a part of the visionary design. Measurements of the size of after-images under various conditions did not reveal anything exceptional. While the visionary phenomena were stationary, the after-images moved with the eyes.

Mayer-Gross and Stein assert that phases in which after-images cannot be produced alternate with phases in which the after-image is unusually strong and lasts longer than usual. Such phasic differences, then, would mean that periods in which the peripheral stimulation is ineffective or almost ineffective are followed by periods in which peripheral stimuli call forth an excessive response. It would be of considerable importance if future work could substantiate such different phases. In the meantime, we note that Mayer-Gross and Stein found them in "almost" all subjects; in other words, the existence of individual differences is admitted. Such individual differences must be also assumed when the question is asked: How do mescal visions and peripheral after-images differ in phenomenal appearance? Observing visions and after-images simultaneously, we found that they did not differ phenomenally. A violet after-image seen e.g. in the midst of a visionary phenomenon turned rapidly into a violet circle which "exploded" into small "stars" which immediately fitted into the visionary design. If in this case one were not to know about the peripheral origin of the violet square, one would consider it a part of the visions. At the same time, we discovered that upon the attempt to touch the gray background, on which the phenomena were observed the finger came into contact with the paper about 20 cm. before the paper. Throughout the observation this paper assumed a cloudy appearance and seemed to "pulsate." In general, in our case visionary phenomena, after-images and real objects were strikingly similar in phenomenological respect. It may be inferred from the above analysis of the visions that this cannot hold in all cases. There are marked differences in the *Erscheinungsweise* of the visions, and in some individuals or in certain phases of the intoxication after-images and visions differ considerably in appearance. Knauer and Maloney found that the peripheral after-images were "much more material and real than the most vivid of the hallucinations produced by the mescaline" and that they were easily distinguishable from the hallucinations. At the same time they report that for some of the subjects the objective character of the visions was so "intense" as to confer upon the vision the "suspicion of real existence," which apparently means that at least in some cases the after-images were not much more material and real than visions. That the after-images finally merge with the visions is reported by the majority of subjects. Knauer and Maloney, although considering visions and after-images as phenomenally dissimilar, remark that "no matter how distinct and how dissimilar the hallucination and the after-image originally were, their ultimate fusion produced an harmonious hallucination." In our observation, such an ultimate fusion took place with open as well as closed eyes, for negative as well as for positive after-images. It is to be noted that the sudden and unexpected appearance of unusually strong after-images, not intently produced during the mescal state, may arouse a slight shock in some individuals.

In connection with after-images the following observation is of interest. Before the visual effects of the drug became manifest "one of the investigated persons . . . carefully studied a map of a region known to him. Among his first hallucinations was a reproduction of this map, in its most minute details; but, in addition to all the details of the map, a town which was actually omitted in the map appeared in its proper position in his hallucinatory representation of the map" (3). We are reminded here of the phenomena of *Sinnengedächtnis* which under certain conditions are observed in everyday life. Here a stimulus object is not only reproduced in all its details, but it is also amplified in a certain way. In other cases, the visionary representation of the object is exact, but certain elements are missing.

Objects normally seen in two dimensions may appear tridimensional in the mescal state. Tridimensional objects may seem still more voluminous than usual. One of the subjects has to discontinue reading in a paper since the shadows of minute folds on the surface of the paper hardly perceptible to the normal eye are too disturbing. The same subject speaks of a general "plasticity—experience." "In such a way, all objects, even the smallest and most unimportant ones, appeared to me massive and as if special emphasis was laid on them intentionally . . . this 'plasticity—experience' was extremely pleasant and it led me to seek for more and more pleasure in plastic and solid things . . . a red paper-square seemed to be a piece of red velvet . . . a whitish gray, rather dirty curtain seemed to be made of cement. This perception was not interfered with by the fact that the 'cement-curtain' was easily moved by the wind. On the contrary, I felt an indescribable joy in seeing such a massive thing moving . . . the design in the white table-cloth was also set-off from the ground which was sort of grayish . . ." (13). Newspapers, pictures, floors, etc. may assume the appearance of relief maps; there may be an increase in the solidity of the furniture and the houses. Looking at a picture representing Naples, one of the subjects finds it "so plastic and life-like" that he believes himself on the beach of Naples. In such a way, there develops a "hyperplastic seeing as in the stereoscope." Human faces seem to undergo certain changes; they become more "expressive," the features become more sharply defined. "The wrinkles seemed to deepen, the shadows to become clearer and more colored; the yellowish-green reflection of the wallpaper led to a tired and cadaverous expression. At the same time, the faces seemed to be more characteristic in their expressions." Some subjects feel that their ability to infer certain traits of personality from facial expressions becomes increased.

The changes in the apparent size of real objects require special consideration. To illustrate: "When I moved my hand towards me, it got enormous and bulky forms . . ."; "I looked out of the window and was particularly surprised at the changes in the size of the houses . . . they seemed to have grown after the fashion of skyscrapers . . ."; "the bread I held in my hand did not become smaller . . . what I bit off at one end, grew again at the other . . ."; "as regards the cutlets and afterwards the cake, I try to determine which is the larger piece, but I do not succeed. I am sure that they are of unequal size, but after every decision it is clearly the other one which is larger . . ."; "the branches (of a tree) became longer and shorter"; "while looking e.g. at the shingler on the roof, he seems to shrink and to grow"; "a special treat was the way Dr. B. was eating; I saw how he opened his mouth wide and how an enormous-appearing potato disappeared in this enormous-looking mouth . . . the mouth and the potato did not appear in larger size, but there was somehow the expression of enormous size in a way now inexplicable to me . . ." (13). In this connection, we may cite the following observation: "The two experimenters seemed to sit far off from me . . . but there was no diminution in size" (13). But: "One time I saw that an object at a distance of about ½m. below my face turned suddenly smaller and receded as if it disappeared in endless depth" (13). We may add a few other cases in which a decrease in size was observed. "All of a sudden I noticed that the letters in the book became smaller. At the same time I did not have the impression that this sensation was somehow caused by an increase in the distance between the book and my eyes"; "in the experiments on after-images I found that the objective pictures presented to me became smaller when moved towards or away from me; they grew the smaller, the faster they were moved. As soon as the stimulus object was standing still, it seemed to assume its normal size" (13).

In most of these cases the object did not lose its normal proportions. The changes reported are rather complex. There may be e.g. an alteration between macropsia and micropsia or a suddenly developing macropsia or micropsia. In addition we may have changes in the perception of distance and movement. Of unusual interest are observations in which in spite of macropsia (or micropsia) the object does not change its size according to the observer. This seems a paradox, but Pick and others have called attention to similar phenomena in pathology. We have obtained reports of this kind from eidetic individuals.[1] The subject above referred to sees a potato of enormous size disappear in the enormous mouth of Dr. B., and yet mouth and potato had "normal size." Such observations cannot be dismissed by saying that the impression of "enormousness" has a non-optical foundation. This may be the case in some instances, but there are too many observations in which the subject considers it as the most adequate description to say that he "sees" an enlarged object and yet, at the same time, experiences no increase in size. Further analysis has to bring out more clearly the components of this phenomenon.

Some of the excerpts quoted above indicate that the perception of movement is also abnormally changed. On the one hand, actually performed movements may be perceived in an abnormal way; on the other hand, stationary objects may perform apparent movements. As regards the first possibility we find e.g. that a person walking through the room is perceived successively at different places or that a person walking downstairs is only seen at three different places of the staircase. Thus the continuous movement of an object is inferred from the successive appearance of this object at different places. A person moving his hand to his face may see it at the beginning and at

[1] For a review of the eidetic literature cf. H. Klüver: Studies on the eidetic type and on eidetic imagery. Psychol. Bull., 1928, 25, 69–104.

the end of the movement. Moving clouds may appear successively at different places. Under certain conditions, the moving
object appears simultaneously at different places. Some excerpts from the Heidelberg records illustrate this phenomenon:
"The perception of a moved burning cigarette was a great
surprise to me. Not a continuous line or circle as seen under
normal conditions in the dark room, but a number of small
glowing balls. At the end of the movement I could still see
the entire movement as if it were fixed by a number of glowing
balls standing in the air. Then these balls jumped all of a sudden
in a great hurry into the glowing end of the cigarette, but always
along the path taken by the cigarette. They did not fade, but
all of them went along the curve to the terminal point just as
if they were connected by a rubber band. Everything was so
distinct that I was able to count the glowing balls; one time I
counted 16; there was no luminous line between the glowing
balls; it was dark . . . the faster the movement, the more a
transition from balls into lines and a decrease in the distance
from each other." Another subject reports: "I perceived that
luminous points appeared successively, about 12–15. The single
points were never connected with each other during the movement. . . . Moreover, the lights which were successively seen
appeared immediately hereafter simultaneously. The simultaneous impression was the strongest." Another person watching the cigarette sees a large number of bright spots flowing
into each other. Still another person sees a continuous luminous
line the different places of which differ in brightness. A subject
to whom on the preceding day Wertheimer's experiment on
apparent movement had been demonstrated was able to see
the phi-phenomenon under normal conditions very clearly. In
the mescal state, the successive exposure of two luminous lines
did not elicit a perception of movement.

The various kinds of abnormal movements described in these
reports are not found in all persons or in all phases of the
intoxication. The results produced by mescal in this respect are
not uniform. As a matter of fact, many individuals see movement as a continuous whole. But such a continuous movement

may be "abnormally slow" and an increase in speed may lead
to "jerky," "strange," "automatic" or "peristaltic" movements.
A further increase, then, will do away with the continuity and
lead to seeing the object successively or simultaneously at
different places. In other words, there are cases in which the
perception of movement varies with the speed of the object.
We hasten to add that there are cases in which this does not
hold at all. We should add, furthermore, that there are observers
who report excessively fast movements. Upon the experimenter's moving a cigarette in the dark room, the subject perceives
this movement e.g. "as desperately fast, as fast as it cannot be
performed by any human being." Or: "When Dr. B. showed me
his watch, I saw the ring (of the chain) in frantic motion which
continued for such a long time as if it would never stop."

There is no doubt that an experimental analysis of the perception of movements in the mescal state will lead to very important results. Even though quantitative data are not at hand
the above cited observations are extremely interesting not only
on account of their bearing on the theory of perception, but
also in the light of results obtained on pathological cases. Here
Best, Pötzl and Redlich, Gelb and Goldstein have made some
important contributions. Thus a patient of Gelb and Goldstein
saw the handle of a stopwatch or a moving light successively
at different places. The same patient was unable to perceive
stroboscopic movement. He could not see the continuous movement of a rod passing over his skin although he was able to
identify the tactual impression.

We shall turn to a consideration of the apparent movement
of stationary objects. Phenomenally, such movements may
differ considerably. There are jerky and undulating movements;
there are movements which change the contours and dimensions of the object, and movements which leave them unaltered
but displace the object as a whole. A package of cigarettes
moves suddenly with a jerk, or the surface of the walls and the
ceiling seems to move back and forth. It is not surprising that
the occurrence of certain apparent movements impresses the
subject deeply. "I saw that the scales of the fish as well as the

fish itself were distinctly moving; I was unable to eat it. I admired the certainty with which Dr. B. was convinced of the death of the fish. The noodles behaved literally and without exaggeration as a moving heap of worms" (13). The same subject tells us that in the moment a bird was about to fly from a window sill, the sill protruded, that the floor-stones of the corridor seemed to contract and to expand; trees, plates, and especially objects with designs appeared to be in constant motion. Another individual reading in a book sees the letters in rapid motion from the left to the right. "Then the letters moved also in the opposite direction, then against each other, constantly changing form and size" (13).

Changes in position of objects due to apparent movements are frequently accompanied by changes in size, color tone, brightness, etc. It is very difficult to single out those factors which principally determine the appearance of objects under such circumstances. The changes are very complex, the "normal" appearance is extremely modified. "I am sitting before a shelf which is attached to the wall and on which there are several bottles, empty glasses and small test tubes. The shelf has not its normal shape; the boards are curved as if they were made of caoutchouc, the whole shelf becomes alternately higher and lower; soon it is leaning towards me, soon it retreats to the wall. Other objects in the field of vision take part in these movements. The bottles also behave as if they were caoutchouc; they fold up as high-hats" (13).

It is theoretically interesting that the occurrence of apparent movements in the mescal state depends to a certain extent on the nature of the stimuli. Certain observations show that small objects are more easily displaced than large ones; objects which together with their surroundings form an optical "whole" and which are so to speak definitely anchored in optical respects are less likely to move than those which seem to be detached from their background; objects the contours of which "suggest" movement are more likely to move than those with definite, well-marked contours; objects the appearance of which gives the impression of weight are less likely to be displaced than those which appear light. It is to be noted that even under normal conditions our apparently stable world involves optically certain tendencies to movement. Whereas in everyday life we may be aware of only this *tendency* we find that in the mescal state this tendency, this implicit *dynamis,* is transformed into actually perceived movement. At this point we have to insist on the fact that it is not necessary at all that the subject be consciously aware of the above mentioned qualitative aspects of the phenomena. It is not necessary, for example, that he consciously judge a given object to be a "very small" object; what matters is not the judgment but the fact that "smallness" or the dynamic aspects above referred to phenomenally exist. If they exist, then, apparent movement is likely to occur. Expressed differently: we find empirically that apparent movement is likely to occur as soon as certain optical characteristics are present. We do not need introspective processes to see that the contours of an object "suggest" movement, involve a definite tendency to movement, as we do not need them for ascertaining the truth that an object is red. It is perhaps not necessary to point out that enumerating a number of optical aspects in the stimulus configuration does not *explain* the existence of apparent movement; we merely state the conditions under which apparent movement is observed. In short, it is the attempt at an analysis of the objective *Umfeld* undertaken with the view to describe as completely as possible the optical conditions under which apparent movement takes place. Our analysis is by no means complete and must be supplemented by an analysis of what *Gestalt* psychologists have called the *inner* Umfeld, the subjective factors. The will to see movement or to suppress apparent movement, the "attitude" of the subject and other factors are, as the records indicate, very important. But at present, our chief concern is to emphasize the importance of some optical aspects of the stimuli in the outer *Umfeld.* These aspects are of great theoretical interest since they are the same as those which have been brought out by the experimental studies on apparent movements in eidetic images. Some studies show that there may be also spontaneously occurring or intentionally produced "displacements" of *real* objects by eidetic individuals. The importance of the same factors is stressed in the literature on visual disturbances in patients with cerebral lesions or with pathological changes in tonus. These researches bring home to us that there are forms, configurations, and events in our optical world which possess a certain *dynamis* which under abnormal conditions or on certain developmental levels becomes apparent in movement.

In general, the behavior of visionary objects and of real objects during the mescal state offers many striking parallels. Thus we have not only diplopia and polyopia of visionary, but also of real objects. The following observations refer to real objects: "Then a patient came to the window and laughed. When he left, there seemed to be two. Suddenly I noticed that the mirror image of these two ran away in the opposite direction . . ."; "somewhat later I fixated a point on the ceiling where I noticed some small flies and cobwebs. All of a sudden the number of the flies seemed to increase . . ." (13). Still more interesting is the following observation: "Being seated before Förster's adaptometer, M. passed me on my left side. I saw nothing but a part of his cloak. Automatically it turned into the whole figure of M.; and I had now some sort of idea that a large number of M.'s moved away from me in a curved line, the M. in the foreground being the smallest one. I was unable to say whether it was a very strong image or a vision; phenomenally, the many M.'s were projected into the perceived space of the dark room." This last example owes its importance to the fact that it suggests the possibility of imaginal polyopia. We might, then, distinguish imaginal, hallucinatory and "objective" polyopia in the mescal state. Here again mescal induces changes irrespective of the distinction between imagery, objective perception and hallucination. One is reminded here of the waste of scientific energy in attempting again and again to bring out the differences between "sensation" and "image" or—to use Hume's terms—between "impression" and "idea." Instead of trying to establish two separate classes of mental experience, a more promising approach might be suggested: the attempt to determine those characteristics with regard to which various kinds of optical experiences such as memory-images, hallucinations, pseudohallucinations, eidetic and hypnagogic images, do not differ.

Some of the observations cited above refer to modifications of the objective stimulus which may be classed as "illusions." In some cases there is a very gradual transformation from a stimulus object into an illusory product; a dirty wall for example may induce the subject "to see things." "On the lime-washed, dirty, grayish-white wall there is a movement of lines, in different depth, against each other, horizontal and vertical . . . the lines could be interpreted, and through the interpretation the picture became more distinct. The middle of the wall was a spot interpreted as a house; small spots made the whole, without effort, into a long, castle-like building; I could see the windows and the ramp. Before them there was an elegant line which represented the shore of a pond in a very plastic way. The castle was reflected in the water. When my interpretative effort weakened, the whole picture persisted for a while, then other ever-changing pictures appeared, forming themselves slowly. At first the lines became always more distinct until something turned up without my being conscious of influencing the whole process . . . it was not possible any more to see nothing but lines, there was always something. . . . I did not succeed in seeing something intentionally without having the lines as a basis" (13). The same subject following in everyday life the procedure of Leonardo da Vinci or Johannes Müller was quite unable to "see" something on walls or ceiling, etc. At the same time, the experimenter found that comparing this subject with others mescal produced "the smallest number of optical phenomena." For another subject some threads lying on a picture turned into balls and filled up the whole picture as sea-nettles. Here the different phases of the transformation are not clear. The following excerpt from a record illustrates such phases especially well: "I had to look . . . at the wall . . . some stripes protruded, others receded, it was not any more a smooth wall though I knew it was a wall. Transparent cupolas appeared, made of fine misty stripes; I could not determine whether they had a basis in the cigarette smoke of the room or in the stripes on the wall . . . sometimes the wall disappeared entirely, yet I had not the sensation of a hole or of meaningless cupolas in an otherwise normal room" (13). Though we may know the general nature of the visions and the behavior of the visual images of a person, it is not possible to predict whether or not he will have illusions or the kind of illusions he will have looking at a given object. The records show that amorphous and very simple forms as well as objects highly differentiated in form and color are the point of departure in the formation of illusions. It seems, however, that optically complex objects are more likely to form a basis for illusory products than optically simple forms.

One may expect that a drug which has in the majority of cases such a striking influence on the optical sensorium will alter the character of the dreams during the period of sleep following the intoxication. In normal life visual elements are predominant in the dreams of most persons; Sante de Sanctis speaks even of a *traduzione visiva* of all elements. One may expect that mescal will accentuate this visual character and that the subjects will report a large number of unusually vivid dreams. The analysis of the observations does not confirm such a view. Unfortunately, in some records no reference is made to dreams. In the following we quote the statements of different observers: "I slept quietly, deeply, and had no dreams"; "I could not sleep for about an hour, but after that I slept relatively well without having special dreams"; "in spite of falling asleep very late a deep dreamless sleep"; "I cannot recall my dreams during the night"; "I could see the star-like pattern in faint colors before my eyes until falling asleep.—No special dreams"; "without sleep until 3 o'clock in the morning, after that unusually plastic, colorful dreams" (13). Personally, the only thing I could recall the morning after the experiment was that I had dreamed of discussing an abstract philosophical problem with a friend. Only one of the seven observers just quoted refers to unusually vivid dreams. The same observer awakening during these dreams was able "to perceive very clearly the dream figures" with open eyes, in the twilight of his room, for about ten seconds. After this period they faded away. The few observations available seem to indicate that an enhancement of visual elements in dreams is the exception rather than the rule.

In this analysis of the psychological effects of mescal we have been chiefly concerned with the visual effects. Emphasizing effects of visual nature we do not mean to imply that only the visual effects in the mescal state are of psychological interest. But it seems that at present the visual analysis is more promising than a consideration of the non-visual changes induced by mescal. Not only on account of the fact that mescal happens to be a drug which causes chiefly visual phenomena, but also because the visual sense belongs to the "objectifying" senses in the terminology of J. v. Kries. Many of the non-visual phenomena arising under the influence of mescal are of such a nature as to make it at present impossible to determine any constants in the flow of experiences. But in spite of the variability of the phenomena in the visual field it does seem possible to evolve for this modality certain criteria as has been already shown. There is no doubt that the general character of the visual experiences in the mescal state as brought out in our analysis cannot be viewed as an isolated datum; this character must be considered in its relation to the changes induced in other sense fields, in the motor field and in the different reaction-systems of the personality.

Although it is not our aim to consider these concomitant changes in full detail we shall state briefly some of the effects noted in other sense fields. In our own case these effects were not very pronounced. "With regard to auditory stimuli, even noises caused by writing, swallowing, etc., seemed to be loud. Tones of my violin had a greater voluminousness than usual. . . . With regard to organic sensations, I seemed to be 'beyond all desires.' I did not feel hungry or thirsty . . . frequently repeated gymnastic exercises seemed to be amusing rather than fatiguing. Walking was performed with remarkable ease." Dr.

Eshner found the sense of taste benumbed and the sense of hearing less acute. One of Beringer's subjects reports "extraordinarily strong odors"; another one describes the smell of soap and powder as disgusting. In one of the subjects of Prentiss and Morgan the sense of smell was blunted to such an extent that he could not tell "whether or not tincture of asafoetida was perfume." As regards taste, it happens for example that all food taken during the mescal state tastes "like water" or that saliva has the taste of good wine. But in general, changes in the olfactory and gustatory fields seem to be rather infrequent. Changes in the auditory field are more frequently referred to. Tones and noises appear very loud and distinct or extremely faint and at a great distance. Over-tones are often noticed. Illusions and elementary hallucinations occur. Sometimes even voices are hallucinated.

The changes produced in the somatopsychic field and in related fields demand a more detailed consideration. We recall in this connection Serko's "haptic hallucinations." Abnormal states of such a kind are also reported by other observers. It is difficult for the experimenter to form a precise idea of the nature of these phenomena on the basis of the descriptions given by the subjects. One person e.g. reports that he "sees and feels" his thorax constantly growing until it becomes a garden in which the arms are alleys. In another case the right half of the body was felt to be continuous with the surroundings. Still another subject found that with regard to his left hand there was no "feeling of continuity" with the rest of the body. A part of the abnormal experiences described by the subjects may be properly designated as abnormal temperature–, pain–, pressure–, touch– or kinesthetic sensations; a part of them does not fit into psychological categories. An abnormal cold sensation is frequently localized in hands, feet or legs; sometimes it seems to spread all over the body. Definitely localized warmth sensations are rather infrequent. Pain sensations are often associated with other sensations. Very often mention is made of unpleasantly toned pressure sensations caused by the clothing. A subject may get rid of his collar on account of a "feeling of strangulation" at his neck.

Objects touched with the hand may feel like "rubber" or "wax." "There was no metal which was hard and offered resistance; the walls also appeared soft." Thus an irresistible tendency to manipulate or to "mould" objects arises. Some objects or even some of the limbs may appear abnormally heavy or without weight. The occurrence of such sensations may eventually throw light on the motor reactions in the mescal state. In this connection, we observe stuporous conditions as well as extreme restlessness. A person in the horizontal position intending to walk may need an assistant to bring him into the vertical position. In one of the cases of Prentiss and Morgan the drug caused such a marked "depression of the muscular system" that the subject was unable to walk or to speak above a whisper.

The following observations picture typical mescal effects: "I lost the feeling of bodily unity. The idea I could put an arm or a leg aside, separated from the body, seemed quite natural to me"; "my arm becomes suddenly long (not optically); leaning against the wall, I believe I shall sink; my coat . . . is to be buttoned only through my belly . . . my nose is of wax . . ." (13). In the last example, visual perception is normal. Sometimes some of the limbs seem to shorten or lengthen, a leg e.g. may seem several meters long; sometimes the whole body "feels to be smaller." The bodily form may be distorted, the limbs may be "swollen" or they may "melt away." Irregular muscular contractions may take place in different parts of the body, yet the subject may doubt that the muscles belong to his body.

An experimental investigation of the sensory and perceptual changes just reported is extremely difficult. The experiments made so far have not yielded any outstanding results.

A few remarks must suffice to characterize the various forms of synesthesia in the mescal state. We may quote some examples from the Heidelberg records: the hearing of rhythmically presented sounds is accompanied by the seeing of small gray circles; disagreeable tones elicit skin sensations; visually perceived movement is accompanied by tactile sensations; bright light elicits a cold sensation. Or: "Whenever I touch something, I have light sensations." Or: "The barking of a dog moved the whole picture and vibrated through my right foot. This was so distinct that I thought it necessary to identify the dog with my right foot." Here we see that an existent visual impression is only modified. In cases of synesthesia the two sensory experiences often present themselves simultaneously.

4

"MESCAL PSYCHOSIS"

"Mais, ce qui est plus important, je crois . . . c'est de connaître l'action du poison sur la partie spirituelle de l'homme. . . ."

BAUDELAIRE

Our discussion has been chiefly concerned with the formal characteristics of the sensory and perceptual phenomena in the mescal state. If we now recall the fact that some investigators speak even of a "mescal psychosis," it becomes apparent that we have neglected important aspects of the psychological picture produced by the drug. Thus for Beringer the three main constituents of the mescal psychosis are: 1, abnormal sensory phenomena; 2, a fundamental change in conscious states and attitudes; 3, abnormal emotional states. He emphasizes the fact that these three "fundamental reactions" may appear independently of each other. For a better understanding of the visual phenomena we shall now discuss some phases in the psychotic state as caused by strong doses of mescal.

Undoubtedly in many instances the subject faces not only an abnormal external world, but also an entirely changed inner world during the mescal state. He has to accept the fact that objective events as well as ego-conditions are changed. But how is he to accept this fact? How is he to react intellectually and affectively to these changes produced by an alkaloid? But his "normal" modes of reaction are also changed; the question, therefore, reduces itself to a consideration of the various changes produced in "ego" and "world," in "subject" and "object," as well as in the subject-object relations. Thus we may observe a distortion of time and space, a modification in thinking and volition, disintegration on different levels of reaction, paranoiac reactions, delusions of reference and persecution, euphoria, and tendencies to "identification." Only a few of these psychotic trends will be discussed here.

Very often the subjective experience of "time" undergoes definite changes. There may be e.g. "no time" or "eternity" or "a large, empty hole." A given period may appear infinitely long or short. The time for answering a simple question may appear to extend over hours. Upon "concentration" it is in most cases possible to make fairly accurate estimates as to duration. Nevertheless, the temporal appearance of real objects is frequently changed in a striking manner. The succession of visionary phenomena may also turn into an "indescribably overwhelming complexity" of a "stationary presence." Such paradoxical states are often associated with the above described disturbances in the perception of movement. Here it is of interest that in one of Beringer's subjects even the ability to imagine the movement, the successive appearance, of a given object was disturbed.

Time distortion and disturbances of associative processes may go hand in hand. Instead of temporal continuity there is a series of disconnected situations which the subject is unable to combine intellectually. A person going to the dark room registers for instance situations of the following kind: "Faces to the left—faces below me—strange corridor never seen before . . . people at the corner . . ." etc. "Every kind of thinking was extremely difficult for me. At first most situations appeared beyond understanding; some of them I did not grasp at all" (13). The ability to organize and to abstract material is lost; the determining tendencies suffer. To concentrate on something for a long while becomes impossible. It is to be noted, however, that some subjects speak of a "thought intoxication," of a state which may prove to be actually quite productive. Such phases of productive thinking are usually of transitory nature.

A study of the Heidelberg records brings out the fact that euphoria is one of the typical mescal symptoms. In spite of marked nausea many subjects "have a good time"; being in a state of mental exhilaration they become talkative and jocular, they commit social errors and enjoy committing them; harmless remarks, even a potato salad or a catsup bottle are considered unusually funny. Sometimes the euphoric state may have no foundation whatever in objective happenings. "Suddenly I noticed that I lost control over myself through my laughing and was forced to continue laughing without any stimulus object." Some subjects refer to "cosmic emotions" and to ecstatic states in which "our exclamations of enjoyment become involuntary." A few records indicate that mescal may cause fear and "horrible depressions"; one of the subjects of Prentiss and Morgan felt "that his life was leaving him." The drug apparently does not influence the sexual sphere in any specific way. The Indian peyote-eaters maintain that it inhibits sexual desires.

In using the term *presque vu*-experience we intended to designate special forms of visual experience. Such experiences may become of central importance in the mescal psychosis. The subject feels e.g. that he is near grasping a "cosmic" truth, but that, unfortunately, he does not quite succeed. A subject seeing a fretwork design may identify "himself" or "everything" with fretwork in the mescal state. Thus certain formal characteristics of the visual phenomena become so to speak the subject matter of the psychosis. The question arises: Is the form of the visual experiences not really the expression of more fundamental changes caused by mescal? If not, is it not at least considerably influenced by changes of such kind? Have the visual phenomena nothing to do with the personality-trends of the subject, with his attitudes, his interests and his complexes? Apparently they have not; at least in most cases there is no relation between the optical picture and the "inner life" of the person. The fact that one subject experiences a fretwork design as a phenomenon to be explained by certain findings in sensory physiology, and that another subject considers it not only of cosmic significance, but as the cosmos itself, is certainly an interesting contribution to the individual psychology of these subjects. But here we want to stress the point that both subjects see the fretwork-design, that means no matter what the reactions of the individual in the mescal state are, mescal produces certain typical visual effects uninfluenced by the personality of the subject. On the basis of our analysis we are able to predict these super-individual effects. But with regard to the psychotic symptoms, Beringer is probably right when he assumes that even on the basis of a very intimate knowledge of the subject it is absolutely impossible to predict the kind of mescal psychosis which he is going to develop. Beringer also asserts that after a careful study of various reports of mescal psychoses we cannot recognize any of them as belonging to this or that subject. So far, definite correlations cannot be established. At least so far as mescal is concerned we question Baudelaire's "Tout homme a le rêve qu'il mérite" and are sceptical concerning Rouhier's hope that this drug may become a tool in the hands of the psychoanalyst. There are interesting individual differences. We see on the one hand the individual with a critical *Einstellung* who naturally or intentionally detaches himself from the phenomena, and on the other hand, the person who experiences or seeks to experience a unity of world and I. Again, there is a long way from the critical attitude to the mere registration of disconnected sensory contents, to the "passivity-syndrome." "I became so to speak a resigned observer who was trying in vain to catch expansive experiential qualities by means of an insufficient schematism, and I became more and more inclined to give up this kind of observation." There may be for a while a rapid shift from one idea to the other, from one sense experience to the other. But finally the subject cannot rid himself of the single experience, it becomes "everything," may it be a thread, a key, a scar, or a plate. All spontaneity being lost it is only this thread or this plate the individual is still conscious of. Or the idea "Dr. M. G." may be the only thing he is conscious of. Thus consciousness is narrowed down to the experience of sensory and imaginal details. But these details expand, they become everything: "I feel to be identical with the object."

This subject-object unity may be experienced in various ways: "It seemed to me as if tones, optical phantasms, body sensations, and a certain . . . taste formed a unity, as if what I experienced in my body and what I experienced perceptually in the external world were not separated any more, as if body and object were a unity" (13). Or: "The line of demarcation drawn between 'object' and 'subject' in normal state seemed to be changed. The body, the ego, became 'objective' in a certain way, and the objects became 'subjective.' They became subjective not only in the sense that they behaved as visionary phenomena, but also in the sense that they gained certain affective qualities" (14).

In some individuals the "ivresse divine" Rouhier speaks of is undoubtedly not very pleasurable; in fact, it is rather an "ivresse diabolique." But in either case it is true that the experiences in the mescal state are not easily forgotten. One looks "beyond the horizon" of the normal world, and this "beyond" is often so impressive or even shocking that its after-effects linger for years in one's memory. No wonder that some of the subjects are disinclined to repeat the experiment and go through experiences which distort the "normal" world.

5

IMPORTANCE FOR RESEARCH

"Il ne faut pas croire que tous ces phénomènes se produisent dans l'esprit pêle-mêle. . . ."

BAUDELAIRE

On account of its specific effects on the optical sensorium mescal is an excellent instrument of research for the psychologist. It is a very handy tool especially in the descriptive and genetic analysis of space and color phenomena. Utilizing this drug we may study profitably various aspects of normal and abnormal visual perception, simultaneous and successive contrast, different types of colorblindness, entoptic phenomena, dreams, illusions, pseudohallucinations, hallucinations, synesthesia, *Sinnengedächtnis*, the relation of peripheral to central factors in vision, the role of visual elements in thinking and the psychogenesis of "meaning." Owing to the subjectification of the "objective" world in the mescal state, an investigation of the last problem seems especially promising. The study of eidetic imagery and of subjective visual phenomena in general may also consider with profit the nature and the behavior of visual phenomena experimentally produced with drugs. Systematic experimentation undertaken with the view to obtaining a complete picture of the optical and non-optical effects in eidetic and non-eidetic individuals, in different constitutional types, in children, in primitives and in individuals of different social level cannot fail to yield definite results. The psychiatrist will be interested in the effects of mescal not only as a means for a more adequate appreciation of the visual disturbances in various diseases, but also as a possible avenue to a psychology of schizophrenia. The anthropologist studying the origin and the varieties of "visions" in different areas or the ornamental art of various tribes will be greatly interested in the existence of certain super-individual form-constants as found in mescal visions.

In general there is no doubt that the form of the visual experiences in the mescal state differs radically from the general form of the visual phenomena caused by other drugs; but in some respects certain drugs lead to remarkably similar visual effects. Psychology, ophthalmology, psychiatry and anthropology are in need of a detailed analysis of the optical effects of various drugs. In fact, a differential pharmacopsychology of form-constants is a desideratum. Unless we know these form-constants, we cannot consider those aspects of the visual phenomena which are due to the personality of the subject. Although at present there seems to be no uniformity in the way personality affects the character of the intoxication, it seems possible that some day the study of mescal effects will give us information about, what Miller has called, "the hinterland of character."[1]

[1] Cf. E. Miller: *Types of Mind and Body*. Psyche Miniatures, 1926.

REFERENCES

1   Ellis, Havelock. Mescal: a new artificial paradise. *Ann. Rep. Smithsonian Instit.*, 1897, pp. 537–48. Washington: Government Printing Office, 1898.

2   Fernberger, S. W. Observations on taking peyote *(Anhalonium Lewinii)*. *Amer. J. Psychol.*, 1923, **34**, 267–70, 616.

3   Knauer, A., & Maloney, W. J. M. A. A preliminary note on the psychic action of mescalin, with special reference to the mechanism of visual hallucinations. *J. Nerv. Ment. Dis.*, 1913, **40**, 425–36.

4   Lewin, L. Phantastica. Die betäubenden und erregenden Genussmittel. Berlin, 1924. Pp. viii + 374. (Cf. also English translation of second German edition: Phantastica. Narcotic and stimulating drugs. New York: Dutton & Co., 1964. Pp. xvii + 335.)

5   Mayer-Gross, W., & Stein, H. Über einige Abänderungen der Sinnestätigkeit im Meskalinrausch. *Z. ges. Neurol. Psychiat.*, 1926, **101**, 354–86.

6   Mitchell, S. W. Remarks on the effects of Anhelonium Lewinii (the mescal button). *Brit. Med. J.*, 1896, **2**, 1625–29.

7   Mooney, J. The mescal plant and ceremony. *Therap. Gazette*, 1896, **20** (whole series), 7–11.

8   Prentiss, D. W., & Morgan, F. P. Anhalonium Lewinii (mescal buttons). A study of the drug, with especial reference to its physiological action upon man, with report of experiments. *Therap. Gazette*, 1895, **19** (whole series), 577–85.

9   Radin, P. (ed.) Crashing thunder. The autobiography of an American Indian. New York and London: D. Appleton & Co., 1926. Pp. xxv + 203.

10 Safford, W. E. An Aztec narcotic *(Lophophora williamsii)*. *J. Heredity*, 1915, **6**, 291–311.

11   Šerko, A. Im Mescalinrausch. *Jahrb. Psychiat.*, 1913, **34**, 355–
      66.

12   Shonle, Ruth. Peyote, the giver of visions. *Amer. Anthropol.*,
      1925, **27**, 53–75.

Cf. also the bibliographies in

13   Beringer, K. Der Meskalinrausch. Seine Geschichte und
      Erscheinungsweise. *Monogr. Gesamtgeb. Neurol. Psy-
      chiat.*, 1927, **49**, pp. iv + 315.

14   Klüver, H. Mescal visions and eidetic vision. *Amer. J.
      Psychol.*, 1926, **37**, 502–15.

15   Rouhier, A. La plante qui fait les yeux émerveillés; le peyotl
      (Echinocactus Williamsii Lem.). Paris: Doin, 1927. Pp.
      xii + 371.

PART II

MECHANISMS OF HALLUCINATIONS

INTRODUCTION

The theories that have been evolved for an understanding of hallucinatory phenomena have frequently stressed one set of factors to the exclusion of others. They have stressed either psychological or physiological factors, "peripheral" or "central" factors, sensory or motor factors, cortical or subcortical mechanisms. In recent years, however, it has been generally recognized that all these factors are of importance. Since all of them are involved in any complex behavioral reaction, it is to be expected that they are involved in hallucinations. An investigator may insist, for instance, that pathological changes in the lens of the eye in conjunction with certain psychological factors are primarily responsible for the appearance of a given hallucinatory phenomenon or that the combined effects of vestibular dysfunction and a lesion of the occipital cortex determine another hallucinatory picture. The fact that certain agents can be found which banish or provoke hallucinations does not mean that the mechanisms involved in bringing about such a result are known. We know at present that hallucinations are influenced by a large number of widely different factors and that they exhibit a wide diversity of phenomenal characteristics. Confronted with these etiological and phenomenal differences, we may ask whether it is possible at all to identify something

"Mechanisms of Hallucinations" appeared as chapter 10 in *Studies in Personality*, edited by Q. McNemar and M. A. Merrill. Copyright 1942 by McGraw-Hill Book Company. Reprinted by permission of the publisher.

like a general "structure" in hallucinations or whether such a structure is dissolved by the operation of heterogeneous factors. In other words, are there any *hallucinatory constants?* This question will be briefly discussed by utilizing certain findings in the literature as well as the author's own studies in the field of eidetic phenomena and his studies of the effects produced by mescaline.[1]

[1] This research has been aided by a grant from the Committee for Research in Dementia Praecox founded by the Supreme Council, Thirty-third Degree, Scottish Rite, Northern Masonic Jurisdiction, U.S.A.

1

HALLUCINATORY CONSTANTS

Mescaline (3, 4, 5-trimethoxyphenethyl amine) has been of unusual interest because of its remarkable psychological and physiological effects (4, 7, 22, 32, 33, 41, 42, 52, 56, 75, 87). Particularly the visual effects have been the subject of many studies. Veit and Vogt (81, 82) injected various alkaloids, including mescaline, into animals, which were then killed to determine the concentration of the poison in different parts of the central nervous system and in other tissues. The amount of mescaline recovered from the occipital cortex of monkeys and dogs did not differ significantly from that found in the frontal cortex. As regards the effects on the optical sensorium, Maloney (46) claimed that injections of mescaline sulfate led to an enormous enlargement of visual fields in "blind or nearly blind" tabetics and to an improvement in visual acuity, as measured by Snellen's test types. Some of the patients were enabled to read who, previous to the injection, could not; one of them went to a motion-picture show. Recently Zádor (88) reported that mescaline restored perception of movement in the hemianopic field of one of his patients (case 6). In this connection, the appearance of the "reddish-blue arcs" of the retina in the mescalinized state is of interest. It is generally agreed that these elliptical reddish-blue arcs, discovered by Purkinje (64), correspond to fibers of the optic nerve, which become entoptically visible (10, 40). Normally, these arcs are very distinct for only a moment, but after an injection of mescaline sulfate the author noticed that they could be seen for a long time.

It is characteristic of the action of many drugs that visual effects predominate. Dominance of visual phenomena, a *traduzione visiva* (Sante de Sanctis), seems to be also typical of deliriums, dreams, and eidetic imagery. As regards the hallucinatory phenomena produced by mescaline, their chief character, according to Havelock Ellis, is their "indescribableness." More than a decade ago, the author raised the question whether it was possible to find any constants in the flow of these "indescribable" experiences and analyzed the available data with reference to the *form* of the hallucinatory material (33). Investigators, such as Berze (5), emphasizing the importance of motor, kinesthetic, or "myopsychic" components in hallucinations, have called attention to the fact that most visual hallucinations are *formed*. There is no doubt that most reports on hallucinations refer to forms of some kind and not to the appearance of visual "dust" or similar material.

The author's analysis of the hallucinatory phenomena appearing chiefly during the first stages of mescaline intoxication yielded the following *form constants:* (*a*) grating, lattice, fretwork, filigree, honeycomb, or chessboard; (*b*) cobweb; (*c*) tunnel, funnel, alley, cone, or vessel; (*d*) spiral. Many phenomena are, on close examination, nothing but modifications and transformations of these basic forms. The tendency towards "geometrization," as expressed in these form constants, is also apparent in the following two ways: (*a*) the forms are frequently repeated, combined, or elaborated into ornamental designs and mosaics of various kinds; (*b*) the elements constituting these forms, such as the squares in a chessboard design, often have boundaries consisting of geometric forms. At times, the boundaries are represented by lines so thin that it may be impossible to say whether they are black or white. Many observers have stressed the fineness of these lines, especially Ceroni (6) and Möller (54). As Möller has pointed out, the "absolute one-dimensional" appears to have become a reality.

For the sake of analysis in terms of "form," we have ignored aspects of color, brightness, and movement, but it is just these aspects which often deeply impress the subject and which he cannot adequately characterize when describing the kaleidoscopic play of forms and patterns. He may, for instance, claim that colors unknown in his previous experience appear; he may even be more impressed by the textures of colors—"fibrous, woven, polished, glowing, dull, veined, semi-transparent" (11); he may insist that the hallucinatory objects consist of materials that are never seen in nature and yet may strangely resemble certain kinds of wood, straw, hair, jewels, wool, silk, or marble. If we ignore the colors and movements as well as the "meaning" with which the phenomena are invested by the subject, the geometric-ornamental structure of the hallucinations becomes apparent. This appears even in the drawings made by artists during or after mescaline intoxication. Such drawings have been published by Szuman (77), Marinesco (48), and Maclay and Guttmann (44).

The fact that certain geometric forms and designs constantly recur has led us to assume certain hallucinatory form constants. Although further analysis may reveal additional form constants, it seems certain that the number of basic forms is limited. At certain stages of the poisoning, the geometric forms and designs may be seen with open as well as with closed eyes, e.g., on the face of a person or on the soup the subject is about to eat. It is significant that the tendency toward these forms may be so strong as to dominate the perception of external objects. One of Beringer's subjects looked at the small branch of a tree and reported: "The leaves . . . suddenly appeared in an ornamental pattern as if joined in a circular design having the form of approximately a cobweb. I looked at other branches, and, looking at them, all leaves assumed the same lattice-like arrangement" (4).

Some or all of the form constants found in mescaline hallucinations are also found in certain hypnagogic hallucinations, in entoptic phenomena, in the visual phenomena of insulin hypoglycemia, and in phenomena induced by simply looking at disks with black, white, or colored sectors rotating at certain speeds

(9, 23, 49, 64, 84). Occasionally they seem even to occur in fever deliriums. One of the patients of Wolff and Curran (86), who happened to be a trained observer and physician, reported that he observed the same hallucinatory phenomenon during four illnesses precipitated by four different agents (measles, malaria, tonsillitis, influenza) at the ages of 8, 12, 30, and 41; he saw a cloud "with a spiral motion shape itself into a brilliant whorl." In two of these illnesses he saw that "brilliantly illuminated green, yellow and red angular crystalline masses shaped themselves into ever-changing patterns like those formed by bits of glass in a revolving kaleidoscope." It can be easily seen from the descriptions and drawings furnished by Purkinje (64) that all the geometric forms and designs characteristic of mescaline-induced phenomena can, under proper conditions, be entoptically observed.

Let us consider, for instance, the form constant for which "funnel," "tunnel," "cone," or similar descriptive terms are used. This form occurs again and again in mescaline hallucinations; it also appears in hypnagogic hallucinations, in entoptic phenomena, and in the phenomena arising when flickering fields are viewed under certain conditions. Or let us consider the "honeycomb" design consisting of hexagons. Purkinje and a number of other observers saw hexagonal patterns entoptically. After awakening in the morning, König (38) frequently noticed, with eyes closed, that his whole visual field was filled up with hexagons (as in a honeycomb). The author saw after awakening, on two different occasions, a pattern almost identical with König's but saw it on the ceiling and not with closed eyes. One of Klien's (31) patients frequently saw, with eyes open, a hexagonal network during migraine attacks. Weil (84) reported that he saw König's design when observing visual phenomena in the hypoglycemic state. The subjects of Haack (23) saw hexagonal patterns when viewing flickering fields. It is clear, therefore, that the honeycomb design, with its hexagonal elements, appears not only in the hallucinatory phenomena produced by mescaline but also under many other conditions. The same is true with respect to the other form constants.

In an "enquiry into the causes of mescal visions," Marshall

(50) has tried to show that the form constants proposed by the author can arise only from some peripheral stimulation that is common to different persons. He accounts for the different form constants by reference to various structures within the eye. It is of special interest that among these he includes retroretinal structures and the choriocapillary circulation. He concludes from anatomical, physiological, and observational data of various kinds that "the rods and foveal cones can look backwards" and that the retinal pigment and the choriocapillary circulation can, therefore, be seen under certain conditions. Similarly, physiologists have attempted to account for entoptic phenomena in general by connecting them with secretions on the cornea, moving particles in the vitreous humor, the network of retinal vessels, the properties and states of the cornea, lens, or other intraocular structures (10, 49).

Hoppe (26), one of the chief exponents of a peripheral theory of visual hallucinations, maintained as early as 1887 that "central (direct, immediate, psychic) hallucinations" arising somewhere in the brain do not exist and that "the entoptic content of the eye" always furnishes the "hallucinatory material." Morgenthaler (55) and others have emphasized peripheral factors even in the hallucinations of dementia praecox patients. Zucker (90) injected mescaline into patients who had hallucinations. As a result of these injections, the tapestry design and modifications of the chessboard design appeared, among other hallucinatory phenomena, in some of his schizophrenic patients. Zádor's patients with tract hemianopia (amaurosis of one eye, blindness in temporal region of other eye) saw, under the influence of mescaline, kaleidoscopic phenomena, squares, and other geometric figures in the whole visual field before both eyes (88). A totally blind patient (amaurosis due to tabes) frequently reported seeing a beautiful chessboard design in the mescalinized state, but he also saw a blue pattern with regularly distributed white points when he was not under the influence of the drug. Mescaline did not induce any visual phenomena in a 23-year-old patient whose eyes had been enucleated during the second year of life.

It must be said that the experiments on patients with some

pathology of the visual system leave so many points unsettled that no general conclusions are warranted. The visual effects, as well as the conditions under which they have been obtained, are often so incompletely described that even available data cannot be interpreted. As Guttmann (21) has pointed out, the crucial experiment with congenitally blind persons still remains to be done. It is a well-known fact that blind persons often report subjective visual phenomena, such as scintillation or photopsiae like "flames" or "sparks," but sometimes they also report definite forms and figures. Whether these figures ever show the patterning indicated in the various form constants described has not yet been systematically investigated. Clear-cut results as to the form constants present in the visual experiences of persons with loss of both eyes or totally blind for other reasons, examined at different intervals after the onset of blindness, are not available.

One of the author's blind subjects (enucleation of left eye, glaucoma of right eye) saw "balls with oval shape," either still or moving, appearing before him at a distance of about 5 feet. The balls were about as large as a dime and were only occasionally colored, chiefly red or violet. He also reported seeing "silver bars," "arabesques," "rings into which you can put your finger," and "shiny test tubes." He claimed that the phenomena were more prominent before his left eye, which had been removed $1\frac{1}{2}$ years ago, and that they did not appear at all on certain days. It was impossible to elicit more definite information. Alternating current did not influence or banish these phenomena. The flicker phenomena that are seen by normal subjects under certain conditions of stimulation with alternating current (65) could not be electrically produced in this subject.

It should be mentioned that the form constants that we have discussed are apparently not typical for the visual phenomena produced by electrical stimulation of the occipital lobe in man. Urban (78) found that the photopsiae consisted mostly of glowing and colored "roundish forms, disks, or rings" when faradic current was used and of stars and ragged forms such as "pointed sparks" when galvanic current was used.

It should be obvious that the factors determining the appearance of certain form constants are so numerous that all theories stressing either "peripheral" or "central" factors are too simple. That there is an interaction of these factors may be true, but this remains in the present state of our knowledge a vague assertion. We wish to stress merely one point, namely, that under diverse conditions the visual system responds in terms of a limited number of form constants. Any general theory, however, will have to go beyond a consideration of visual mechanisms per se. The mescaline-produced phenomena demonstrate this point in a striking manner. Mescaline induces changes not only in the visual field but also in other sensory spheres, particularly in the somatosensory sphere. "Haptic hallucinations" and other somatosensory phenomena may dominate the symptomatology to the exclusion of phenomena in the visual sphere.

We shall not enter into a description of the somatosensory changes, but merely mention that Professor Forster (16), for example, felt a net similar to a "cobweb" on his tongue: "When I opened my mouth, a cold wind passed through and the net moved." Serko (72) frequently had the sensation that his legs or his feet consisted of "spirals." In his case, sometimes the haptic spiral of a leg blended with a luminous spiral that had been rotating in the visual field. "One has the sensation of somatic and optic unity." To dismiss such phenomena as synesthetic experiences merely emphasizes the present lack of knowledge concerning the processes involved in synesthesias and intersensory relations in general. A physician, a subject of Beringer (4), "saw" and "felt" the sounds of a concertina played by the experimenter, and the pain produced by it coagulated as luminous curves in the spiral turns of his body, the lower part of his body being a green varnished cone with spiral windings. Such experiences would probably be classified as instances of complex synesthesias. However, a form constant may involve so many spheres that even a synesthetic basis would be too narrow. In one of Beringer's subjects (also a physician), the "lattice" or "fretwork" constant became so dominant that it appeared to penetrate the whole personality.

The subject stated that he saw fretwork before his eyes, that his arms, hands, and fingers turned into fretwork and that he became identical with the fretwork. There was no difference between the fretwork and himself, between inside and outside. All objects in the room and the walls changed into fretwork and thus became identical with him. While writing, the words turned into fretwork and there was, therefore, an identity of fretwork and handwriting. "The fretwork is I." All ideas turned into glass fretwork, which he saw, thought, and felt. He also felt, saw, tasted, and smelled tones that became fretwork. He himself was the tone. On the day following the experiment, there was Nissl (whom he had known in 1914) sitting somewhere in the air, and Nissl was fretwork. "I saw him, I felt him; Nissl was I."

It seems necessary to assume some basic process operative in different sense modalities to cope with all varieties of synesthetic experiences. Even the fact that a sensory impression or a hallucination in one of the sense fields is followed by manifestations in other sense fields does not give us the right to speak of "primary" and "secondary" sensations (or hallucinations) except in the sense of a temporal succession. One event may be primary and another one secondary in this sense, and yet the intersensory relation may involve only one basic process. Similarly, we may doubt whether the preceding example of a "mescal psychosis" with "fretwork" or "lattice" as the central theme can be understood by considering the hallucinatory occurrence of the fretwork in the visual field as the "primary" event that determines "secondary" and "tertiary," etc. events, such as changes in other sense fields and in the mechanisms of thought and emotion.

In a further search for hallucinatory constants, we shall again start with a consideration of the form factor. We note that a single form (figure, object) may be duplicated or multiplied, that its size may change or that its shape may be altered or distorted; i.e., we may have monocular or binocular diplopia or polyopia; dysmegalopsia (micropsia or macropsia); metamorphopsia or dysmorphopsia.

If we analyze the visual phenomena produced by mescaline, we find diplopia, polyopia, dysmegalopsia, and dysmorphopsia not only of hallucinatory objects but also of real or imaginal objects. That is to say, the same mechanisms may be operative, no matter whether an object is perceived, imagined, or hallucinated. The mescaline experiments demonstrate, therefore, that we must go beyond the level of visual hallucinations to determine hallucinatory constants. In fact, we must even go beyond the visual mechanisms that cut across distinctions between perception, imagery, and hallucination and raise the question whether similar mechanisms are operative in nonvisual spheres. There is no doubt that polyopia, dysmegalopsia, and dysmorphopsia find their parallel in experiences in the somatosensory sphere. Subjects in the mescalinized state feel that their limbs shrink or grow, that they are shortened or elongated, or that they are distorted in many ways. The experience of changes in size and the sensation of distortions and alterations may involve the whole body. As regards polyopia, its counterpart is found, for example, in a "polymelia" of the fingers or of the arms. The subject may feel several arms growing out of his shoulder until he feels "like the Buddhas." At times, the alterations in the somatosensory sphere may be so profound that parts of the body feel separated from the rest. As Serko insisted, there may be, not a "sensation" but a "somatopsychic hallucination" of two bodily forms, e.g., of an amputated leg and of a foot entirely separate lying beside it.

The tendency toward reduplication appears not only in polyopia and "polymelia" but also in hallucinatory experiences involving the presence of one or many persons in the room. Although these persons are not seen, their reality is in some way experienced or "felt." In this connection, it is of interest that "splitting" of personality and various degrees of "depersonalization" have been frequently reported. It may be said, therefore, that polyopia, dysmegalopsia, and dysmorphopsia involve mechanisms that are characteristic of mescaline-induced phenomena not only in the visual sphere (hallucination, imagery, perception) but also in the somatosensory sphere.

Further analysis reveals the fact that mescaline is only one of many agents bringing about polyopia, dysmegalopsia, and dysmorphopsia. Thus, under certain conditions, the same effects can be observed in "psychogenic" and "nonpsychogenic" hallucinations, even in the *hallucinations autoscopiques*, in the perception of real objects, in visual imagery, in dreams, in eidetic imagery, in hypnagogic hallucinations, in the phenomena that arise when flickering fields are viewed (4, 12, 14, 15, 23–25, 29, 36, 51, 53, 58, 66, 69, 83, 84). In other words, reduplication or changes in size or shape of a given visual form may occur, no matter whether the object in question is real or has appeared as the result of looking for a considerable time at a flickering field; whether it is hallucinated, visually imagined, or seen as an eidetic or hypnagogic image. In fact, some spontaneous drawings seem to exhibit similar tendencies, so that Maclay, Guttmann, and Mayer-Gross speak of a "mescaline type" of drawing (45). By way of summary, it may be said that polyopia, dysmegalopsia, and dysmorphopsia occur not only in visual hallucinations but also in many other phenomena of the visual sphere (visual perception, eidetic imagery, dreams, etc.).

The fact that diverse visual phenomena commonly assigned to different functional levels of the visual system may show the same typical behavior becomes of still greater interest if we consider the various conditions and clinical states in which such typical behavior occurs. The "symptoms" of polyopia, dysmegalopsia, and dysmorphopsia have been observed in different psychoses, especially in toxic psychoses or at the beginning of certain psychoses, in deliriums, in insulin hypoglycemia, in hysteria, in patients with cerebral lesions, particularly with parieto-occipital or occipital lesions, in the basedoid constitution, in eidetic individuals, and in poisonings produced by certain drugs (hashish, cocaine, etc., chronically used). Beringer (4) has called attention to the existence of these symptoms in the acute phases of schizophrenia. The symptoms were especially striking in one of his hebephrenic patients. Gurewitsch (18, 19) has described an "interparietal syndrome" in which polyopia, dysmegalopsia, and dysmorphopsia are combined with alterations in the postural model of the body or in the bodily schema (Head). According to him, this syndrome is found in nosologically different diseases, such as *lues cerebri*, epilepsy, schizophrenia, hysteria, and cerebral trauma. Thus, the optical symptoms are paralleled in the somatopsychic sphere in other conditions as well as in mescaline intoxication.

In trying to account for polyopia, dysmegalopsia, and dysmorphopsia, ophthalmologists have stressed the importance of dioptric and retinal conditions. Such conditions, however, are not likely to explain the occurrence of similar visual changes in imaginal objects or the fact that the alterations selectively affect only specific objects in a room or only parts of certain objects. Since the optical symptoms occur under many different conditions and in diseases with different etiology, the relative importance of the various factors influencing the visual mechanisms may be expected to vary in different conditions or from one disease to the other. However, we should not necessarily expect entirely different factors to become operative if polyopia and related symptoms appear in a schizophrenic, a mescalinized or eidetic individual or in a patient with a parieto-occipital lesion. The search for some basic factor underlying the optical symptoms in etiologically different conditions is undoubtedly surrounded by the same difficulties as the search for so-called neurological syndromes in psychoses. The "interparietal syndrome" of Gurewitsch is present, for instance, not only in patients with cerebral lesions but also in schizophrenic patients in whom such lesions are absent. It would be rash to conclude that the same syndrome is produced by two different agents. Unfortunately, we are far from knowing the pathophysiological mechanisms that become operative as the result of a parieto-occipital lesion. Once the nature of these mechanisms is known, we shall perhaps understand why the same symptoms may appear, for instance, in schizophrenic patients.

The diversity of conditions in which polyopia, dysmegalopsia, and dysmorphopsia occur has not deterred investigators from looking for some fundamental mechanism. That such a mechanism must be assumed is strongly suggested by the fact that polyopia and related symptoms are characteristic not only of different functional levels in the visual sphere (perception, imagery, hallucination, etc.) but also of the somatosensory sphere. In recent years, the analysis of these symptoms has led most investigators to assign a fundamental role to vestibular factors. It is thought that reduplication of objects, micropsia, macropsia, and dysmorphopsia in hallucinations are indicative of a vestibular influence. The same conclusion is reached, for example, by Menninger-Lerchenthal (53) in his thoroughgoing analysis of autoscopic hallucinations. His view is that autoscopy is a hallucination of the bodily schema which has a visual and a tactile-kinesthetic component. He believes that it does not make any difference whether the study of autoscopic hallucinations is approached from the phenomenological angle or from facts of brain physiology, since the analysis always leads to vestibular factors. Skworzoff (74) has presented similar views. Other investigators have emphasized tonic, postural, and oculomotor factors. In this connection, it is of interest that Pötzl and Urban (63) have stressed the importance of the supravestibular system (in the sense of Muskens).

The experimental data on the influence of the vestibular apparatus on the visual sphere are rather meager. Most of the experiments have been concerned with determining the effects of various forms of labyrinthine stimulation (rotation, galvanic, or caloric stimulation) on different visual phenomena. There is no doubt, however, that the available anatomical, clinical, and experimental data are sufficient for supporting the view that any future research directed toward elucidating the role of the vestibular system is bound to yield extremely significant results not only for the study of hallucinations but also, as some neurologists and psychiatrists insist, for a deeper understanding of neurotic and psychotic behavior. It has even been maintained, particularly by French neurologists, that great strides will be made in psychiatry by obtaining data on vestibular chronaxy.

At this point, it is not possible to outline the various experimental problems that urgently require a solution. We shall be content with calling attention to a new technique that may be employed in analyzing different factors influencing hallucinations or other subjective visual phenomena. By applying alternating current of low intensity and frequency, it is possible to produce flicker that is visible with open or closed eyes under conditions of light as well as dark adaptation. During recent years, the author has obtained some data on the behavior of negative after-images, eidetic images, and hallucinations in the presence of electrically produced flicker. For evaluating the flicker phenomenon itself, it was necessary to examine patients with some pathology of the visual system (hemianopia, enucleation of one eye, etc.). In general negative after-images disappear almost entirely or change radically in appearance the moment the stimulating current is turned on. Cessation of electrical stimulation immediately leads to a reappearance of the after-image and to a restoration of its normal properties. Eidetic images and certain types of hallucinations may vanish, change, or remain unaltered upon appearance of the electrically produced flicker.

To illustrate: one subject, a student, saw an eidetic image of the face of a person looking at him. When the current was turned on, he suddenly saw the profiles of five faces looking to the right. These faces rapidly changed into other faces; they were seen through the "muslin curtain" of the flicker, as the subject expressed it. More than three decades ago, Urbantschitsch (79, 80) used galvanic current for influencing eidetic images. He reports, e.g., that one of his subjects saw an eidetic image of a hepatica. Application of the galvanic current immediately led to the appearance of a large number of hepaticas. It should be realized, of course, that rotation of the subject or electrical and other forms of stimulation may merely accentuate tendencies inherent in eidetic imagery and other subjective phenomena, since polyopia and related visual changes frequently occur in the absence of any stimulation.

To sum up, in our search for hallucinatory constants we have found (a) that the reduplication of objects and the alterations in size and form occurring in hallucinations occur also in other visual phenomena and in phenomena of the somatosensory sphere; (b) that these symptoms appear under many different conditions and in diseases of different etiology. The involvement of different senses and the occurrence of these symptoms in etiologically different conditions suggest that we are dealing with some fundamental mechanisms involving various levels of the nervous system. To elucidate these mechanisms, we must rely on future research to provide the necessary anatomical, pathological, biochemical, and clinical data. Some investigators have advanced the view that tendencies toward reduplication of objects and toward seeing or feeling objects "enormously large" or "very small" or distorted in certain ways satisfy certain intellectual or emotional needs. Let us assume that there is a desire to reduce a dignified person to Lilliputian dimensions "because he will look so funny." The desire itself is likely to be ineffective in producing micropsia unless it is coupled with a basedoid constitution, some disease process, or some other condition that throws certain neural mechanisms into gear. In fact, emotional or intellectual needs of such a kind, if they should exist, may be merely another expression of the existence of such mechanisms. At any rate, there is an interdependence of many different factors.

A further point should be emphasized. We may say that under normal and pathological conditions certain mechanisms are available for producing a limited number of fundamental alterations in a visual object. Such alterations manifest themselves in polyopia, dysmegalopsia, and dysmorphopsia. But the fact that an alteration, e.g., in shape, occurs as one of a limited number of fundamental alterations does not mean that there is any constancy in the sense that particular shapes or distortions are invariably produced. It seems as though there were no limit to the number of different shapes an object may assume in the visual experiences of different subjects. Every conceivable distortion has been reported. The situation is similar with regard to alterations in size or number of objects. A few fundamental alterations may, therefore, produce phenomenologically a very complex picture, especially since changes in number, size, and shape of objects may combine in many ways. Furthermore, all these changes may occur within the framework of altered spatio-temporal relations. For example, the perception of movement may be radically changed or even become impossible; all objects may appear at the same distance, or they may recede into space without changing size (porrhopsia).

In determining hallucinatory constants, we have so far been

primarily concerned with the properties or changes of single objects and configurations. Our next step is to consider the behavior of these objects in space and the relation of objects to each other. We shall start from certain facts obtained in experimental investigations of eidetic imagery (34–36, 68–70).

In studying the behavior of certain types of eidetic imagery, we find an occurrence of the following changes: there is a translocation of objects or parts of objects; parts or properties of one object are transferred to another object; only fragments or certain parts of an object appear; the appearance of one object is accompanied by the disappearance of another; an object undergoes rotational displacements of various kinds (mirror reversals, etc.); there occurs a splitting up of objects into many fragments; objects appear that did not constitute parts of the preceding stimulus situation; a given object disappears and reappears periodically; objects or parts of objects are entirely missing; objects that appeared in the stimulus situation are missing but appear after relatively long periods of time, even after hours, in the eidetic image of some other stimulus situation. The changes just described are characteristic of eidetic images produced by previous stimulation, e.g., by letting the subject view a picture for a certain length of time. But it should be remarked that changes occurring in spontaneous eidetic images are often similar in nature.

It is perhaps safe to assume that these changes involve some basic mechanisms, since similar changes in spatio-temporal relations have been found to occur in visual agnosia. The fact that the visual perception of patients with traumatic lesions of the occipital lobes should exhibit the same type of spatio-temporal changes as certain eidetic images is, as Schilder (68) puts it, "exceedingly surprising" to anybody familiar with the facts of brain pathology. Pötzl (62) has called attention to the fact that even the perceptions of normal persons may show similar changes under conditions of peripheral vision and in tachistoscopic experiments. It is of special interest in this connection that Pötzl (61) was able to produce visual hallucinations by tachistoscopic exposures of pictures or objects in a patient with latent hemianopia and an alcoholic hallucinosis. The experimentally produced hallucinations were characterized by changes of the kind found in eidetic imagery. It is apparent that similar changes are characteristic of dreams. In brief, under certain conditions, the same structure of spatio-temporal transformations becomes apparent in eidetic imagery, hallucinations, dreams, and visual perception.

In an attempt to define hallucinatory constants, we have purposely taken visual forms and their interrelations as a point of departure. It is obvious that we have ignored many aspects of hallucinatory phenomena in order to arrive at these constants. *The hallucinatory constants that we have found may be tentatively assigned to three levels: (a) the level of "form constants"; (b) the level of alterations in number, size, and shape (polyopia, dysmegalopsia, dysmorphopsia); (c) the level of changes in spatio-temporal relations.* We have shown that the same constants appear in other visual, and even in nonvisual, phenomena. These constants are, therefore, not specific for hallucinations but represent general characteristics. The "structure" of hallucinations is a general structure that is typical of numerous phenomena in the visual sphere.

2

THE CONTENT OF HALLUCINATIONS

Since we have been interested in an analysis in terms of formal criteria, we have paid no attention to the *content* of the hallucination. If a childless woman hallucinates many babies, it is readily assumed that the hallucination represents a "projection" of affective needs. But if it should be found that the same woman, when looking at a pencil or a chair, suddenly sees a row of pencils or a row of chairs, it appears unlikely that emotional factors are responsible for the multiple seeing of objects. Of course, any object, no matter whether it is eidetically seen, hallucinated, imagined, or perceived as a real object, may be of emotional significance. It is one thing to admit that objects in multiple vision may have emotional significance; it is an entirely different thing to assert that polyopia itself is created by emotional factors. One of Schilder's (67) patients, an officer with a crippled arm, saw in a fever delirium all persons around him with crippled or missing arms and legs. A blind patient hallucinated heads with empty eye sockets. Following an ophthalmological examination, a schizophrenic woman stated that one of her eyes was red and inflamed; subsequently she saw all persons in the room as having one red eye (53).

It may be said that in such cases of transitivism, to use Wernicke's expression, affective factors determine the content of the hallucination. However, to say that the "projection" of disturbances in the motor, vasomotor, and cenesthetic spheres, or of other disturbances, occurs on an affective basis is an empty statement and adds nothing to our knowledge of the workings of affective mechanisms. We want to know the exact nature of these mechanisms in a given case. That a particular object should appear in a hallucination under the stress of some affective need is not more surprising than the fact that the perception of objects, even of a black line, may be "modified" by affective factors.

Psychologically, objects per se have no existence; they exist only as nodal points in a network of perceptual, affective, or logical relations. It is the determination of these relations that is the task of psychology. A live bull snake, a boa constrictor in a motion picture, and a wavy black line of certain dimensions may lead to reactions of "fear" in a certain monkey, whereas a live garter snake and a boa constrictor in a film running at a higher speed may not. It is not a certain size, color, shape, or speed of movement that leads to the manifestation of "fear" in the monkey but a specific form of "togetherness" of these properties that constitutes the behaviorally effective stimulus, and this can be determined only experimentally. We cannot specify the psychological nature of the "fear" existing in the animal without specifying the effective stimulus properties existing outside the animal. Certain objects or events become emotionally equivalent because they share certain properties. By studying the properties of equivalent and nonequivalent situations, we may be able to learn something about the nature of the affective mechanism. Under the influence of *different* affective factors, objects and events become imbued with *different* properties, just as under one set of conditions a circle becomes perceptually "similar" to and, under another set of conditions, "different" from an ellipse. The affective mechanism in a crippled patient who hallucinates the absence of a leg not only in other persons but also in their photographs and mirror images, as well as in dogs and chairs, is undoubtedly not the same as the affective mechanism in Schilder's patient, who saw his defect only in other persons.

As far as dreams are concerned, a widely held theory explains their content by reference to affective factors. It is assumed that all dreams are wish fulfillments. According to this theory, the appearance of certain objects and events in a dream is determined by some egocentric wish. Certain considerations are pertinent here.

Objects and events, no matter whether they exist in the external world, in a hallucination, or in a dream, may be similar and dissimilar in many respects. To understand particular forms of similarity, we have recourse to mechanisms of sensory organization, to affective factors, to logical relations, etc. The author previously pointed out (37) that it is by virtue of certain similarities that heterogeneous objects and events lie in the same "dimension" or belong to the same "series" and that the problem of determining basic mechanisms in animal and human behavior often reduces itself, therefore, to determining and locating properties or factors in terms of which diverse objects and events may become similar.

It may be said that the behavioral reactions of animals as well as the perceptual and affective reactions or processes of "abstraction" in man proceed by constantly shifting "dimensions," i.e., by constantly destroying similarities and constantly creating new ones. The existence of similarities presents, therefore, no problem; the only problem consists in determining just why particular similarities exist. The occurrence of similarities, i.e., the fact that there exist certain characteristics, factors, or processes that bind objects together and relate them in many specific ways, seems to be of such fundamental nature that the physiologist, Kries, considered it simply an expression of some basic property in the functioning of the central nervous system. Freud, for instance, was forced to the conclusion that the factor of similarity is of paramount importance in the mechanism of dream formation. Since the fundamental role of similarity is apparent in any other group of psychological phenomena, it is not surprising that any superficial analysis of dreams leads to the same result.

However, we must demand that the analysis of the phenomena will provide the *particular* factors that account for the specific ways in which objects and events are related. To account for particular similarities, factors ranging from physical *Gestalten* to castration complexes have been advanced. It is not the large range of such factors that presents a serious problem; the chief difficulty lies in determining which particular factor accounts adequately for certain relations between objects and events, whether it is, for instance, "visual asymmetry" or "fear of bodily injury."

We recall that in eidetic images and certain other phenomena we find translocation of objects or transfer of certain characteristics of these objects, fusions and composite formations, substitutions, the appearance of parts instead of wholes, the non-appearance or the belated appearance of objects or parts of objects, reversals of right and left, up and down, or of other directions. In other words, we find condensation, displacement, and other mechanisms that have been considered typical of dream formation. In eidetic individuals, similar changes may occasionally appear in the perception of real objects and thus become more easily amenable to an experimental approach. From various studies, it is evident that phenomenal properties of objects, visuo-spatial factors, and motor factors play a great role in effecting condensations, displacements, and similar changes in eidetic imagery. *This suggests the possibility that the changes in dreams, such as condensations and displacements, frequently result from an operation of the same (visuo-spatial, motor, etc.) factors.*

In eidetic images, some of these changes can be experimentally demonstrated by setting up certain conditions. The fact that colors, shapes, movements, etc. occur at all in eidetic images, dreams and related phenomena can be understood only by reference to some fundamental properties and processes in the visual system; it seems that the occurrence of certain condensations and displacements can be accounted for only on a similar basis. It should also be recalled that G. E. Müller went so far as to consider the behavior of the eidetic images studied by Urbantschitsch as an example of the influence of "apsychonomic" (anatomico-physiological or metabolic) factors. Urbantschitsch was able to produce a variety of changes in eidetic images by a compression of blood vessels or by the application of visual, auditory, thermal, and other stimuli. At any rate, if visuo-spatial factors lead, for instance, to the fusion of several houses or persons into one, the condensation itself is obviously not created by some affective reaction toward nudity or some similar factor, although, once created, it may still serve as a vehicle for affective needs.

To understand the occurrence of certain spatio-temporal changes in visual phenomena, we must have recourse not only to such factors as brightness, color, shape, and spatial organization but also to factors by virtue of which colors and geometric figures, colors and melodies, sounds and lines may become similar and belong to the same "dimension." Recently, it has even become necessary to resort to "physiognomic characters" to account, for instance, for the similarity between a handwriting, a painting, and the gait of a person. We merely wish to emphasize that the operation of visual factors alone may lead to reversals, displacements, condensations, etc. This does not mean that numerous other factors may not play a role. In an experimental study, Pötzl (62) found that the development of dreams was determined by visual, motor, and "symbolical" factors and that the first two factors were "relatively independent of psychoanalytical factors." He believes that "repressed psychic material," being itself *Gestalt*-less, may act like a catalyzer for optical and motor processes. Whether the psychic material is "repressed" or not does not concern us here, but it is obvious that any color, shape, movement, reversal, displacement, condensation, etc., once supplied by visual or motor processes, may become imbued with "meaning" and that "meaning," in turn, may guide visual and motor reactions.

There is no question that all these factors are also operative in the visual perception of the outer world, but the spatio-temporal stability of external objects is such that fusions, displacements, and the like do not occur in general. Dreams, it has been said, are similar to "eidetic images of the basedoid type." They seem at least similar in that the visual "stuff" they are made of is more open to an invasion of psychic factors than the "stuff" of other visual phenomena. The visual "stuff" provided by entoptic phenomena, flickering fields, ink blots, dreams, eidetic images of the basedoid type, pseudohallucinations, and certain types of hallucinations is apparently more easily invaded by psychic factors than the "stuff" furnished by the perception of real objects, after-images, eidetic images of the tetanoid type, mescaline hallucinations, and certain other types of hallucinations. It is for this reason that phenomena of the first type have frequently been utilized to learn something about the deeper layers of "personality." *If, for physiological reasons, sleep should suddenly provide us with phenomena of Sinnengedächtnis or belated after-images instead of dreams, even "repressed" wishes would not succeed in changing and distorting the visual material.*

At this point, attention should be called to certain facts that may prove to be of interest in connection with physiological or psychological studies of dreams. Since, in most dreams, visual elements are dominant and since striking alterations in the visual sphere are characteristic of mescaline effects, it seems reasonable to expect an enhancement of dream phenomena under the influence of mescaline. An analysis of available data, however, indicates that most subjects report an absence of dreams for the night following the intoxication, and others refer only to "ordinary dreams." Even though the night may have been dreamless, the next day often provides evidence that the visual system has not yet returned to its normal state. In the literature, the author found only one reference to "unusually plastic, colorful dreams," the nature of which was not described (4). It seems, therefore, that, contrary to our expectations, mescaline does not lead to an enhancement of dreams and that it may even suppress dream activity. This can be only a tentative conclusion, since the whole problem has not been systematically investigated. We know nothing about the effects in chronic mescalinism.

Ludlow (43), who has given the most detailed account of the effects of chronic hashish intoxication, points out that his rest was absolutely dreamless during the whole progress of his hashish life, whereas "he never slept without some dream, more or less vivid" before acquiring the habit. "The visions of the drug entirely supplanted those of nature." Further research should explore the mechanisms of drugs which, under certain conditions, produce striking visual effects in the waking state and at the same time do not increase or even suppress dreams, i.e., phenomena that are primarily visual in nature. In contrast to mescaline and hashish, drugs such as alcohol may turn sleep into a *sommeil vigile* that is constantly interrupted and haunted by extremely vivid dreams ("200 dreams in a night"). According to Epstein (13), such effects are particularly characteristic of the prepsychotic phases of alcoholic psychoses. This author even speaks of a "hypnagogic form of alcoholic insanity," since the long-lasting and colorful hypnagogic images in such alcoholics become frequently the starting point for various delusions.

The self-observations of the writer confirm the impression gained from the literature that the night following the mescaline intoxication is either dreamless or practically devoid of visual dream elements. In one of the author's experiments, he saw, on awakening in the morning after a dreamless night, that the kaleidoscopic play of mescaline patterns was still present. The patterns were predominantly violet and could be seen with open or closed eyes. He fell asleep again. During this period of sleep he had a dream that may be properly called a "mescaline" dream.

I am lying in bed in a large hall. It seems to me that there are many similar beds in this hall which are also occupied. I turn over to my right side and see a large window which I subject to close inspection. I see clearly the following black letters R E S T A U R. It surprises me that I can even distinguish letters. To the right of the last R is a vertical pipe, and I am aware of the fact that it covers additional letters. In the window is a large bottle containing red liquid. There are three words on this bottle. These words are complete and meaningful; yet I am dissatisfied with the third word, because I feel that it is somehow too short. The words are surrounded by a reticulated pattern in delicate greenish colors giving the effect of a decorative label. The scene suddenly shifts, and I find myself looking at the gray wall of

a house. Very delicate and fragile objects resembling unshelled pea-
nuts are regularly distributed over the whole surface, thus forming
a latticelike pattern. Each husk stands on end, forming an angle of
approximately 45 degrees with the surface of the wall. Violet clouds
pass across the surface. This makes me wonder whether the whole
phenomenon is merely a hallucination. To determine whether such is
the case I close my eyes; but I still see violet clouds. I conclude that
the house and the peanut lattice have objective existence and that
the violet clouds are of hallucinatory origin.

At this point, we cannot undertake an analysis of this dream
with reference to mescaline phenomena in general and the
phenomena experienced on the preceding day or consider it in
the light of other psychological factors. We merely wish to state
that the mescaline structure of this dream is fairly obvious and
that its mescaline-determined elements range from *presque vu*
experiences (33) to mescaline patterns on objects.

In studying hallucinatory and related phenomena in the visual field, we find that they are interrelated in many ways, not
only in terms of certain "constants" but also in the sense that
the *same* content is experienced on different levels or that a
transformation in content is accompanied by a transition from
one level to another. It is, of course, well known that the same
content may again and again appear on the same visual level,
e.g., in an eidetic image, in a hallucination, or in a dream, etc.
An eidetic subject may always see the same red cap or the same
house when he closes his eyes. One of Ewald's patients (14)
saw in three different deliriums the same three huge brown
dogs with blue eyes entering his room, except that the third
time they suddenly opened their mouths and said, "But this
time it's really we." In contrast, we have the appearance of the
same content on different visual levels, e.g., when a visual scene
experienced in a fever delirium in childhood reappears several
decades later in a mescaline hallucination. Guttmann (20) describes a mescaline hallucination that reappeared as a hypnagogic image 2 years later, when one evening he fell asleep
after an exhausting day during the First World War. He recognized the identity of the content only when he studied old
protocols 5 years afterward. It has also been reported that the

content of a hypnagogic image may reappear in a dream. A mescaline hallucination may be the reproduction of a previously perceived visual object, such as a geographical map. In the experience of the individual, a visual memory-image may transform itself into an eidetic image; a positive or negative afterimage, into a mescaline hallucination; and a pseudohallucination, into a hallucination.

3

"HALLUCINATIONS" VS. "SYNDROMES WITH HALLUCINA-TORY ELEMENTS"

Although it may be true that the complexity of visual hallucinations and related phenomena is somewhat reduced by an analysis which shows that the same constants or even the same contents appear on different visual levels, it does not alter the fact that there still remain many phenomenal characteristics and forms of behavior in hallucinations, eidetic images, dreams, etc., which are refractory to such an analysis. For example, if we consider the phenomenology of mescaline-induced hallucinations, we find "primitive" as well as "scenic" or "panoramic" hallucinations or, expressed differently, "mescaline-specific" and "mescaline-nonspecific" hallucinations (91). It should be remarked that our analysis has been largely confined to "primitive" or "mescaline-specific" hallucinations. Furthermore, it is clear that the total picture of "primitive" and "scenic" mescaline hallucinations is related to changes in other sense fields and ultimately can be understood only by also considering alterations affecting the total personality. We are undoubtedly safe in assuming that the hallucinatory phenomena in a mescalinized person dictating a description of his visual experiences to an assistant are in some way not the same as those of a person in a "mescal psychosis." Kinnier Wilson (85), for instance, refers to an individual who, under the influence of mescaline, was found "crawling about the floor with extreme care, but averred he was a fly walking on the ceiling upside down and that if he moved quickly he would fall and be injured."

In applying the term *hallucination* to phenomenologically and genetically different phenomena, most investigators have tacitly assumed that they are dealing with the "same" symptom and that criteria employed in studying, for instance, visual hallucinations are also applicable to hallucinations in other fields. However, a "hallucination" always appears as an element in a complex of other symptoms. Schröder (71) doubts, therefore, that there is such a thing as a "hallucination," i.e., something which, as an elementary symptom, can be detached from other symptoms and independently studied by comparing it, for instance, with "hallucinations" in other sense fields. He insists that only the whole complex of symptoms, in which the hallucinations appear, can be profitably studied and describes four such "complexes with hallucinatory elements": (*a*) deliriums; (*b*) verbal hallucinosis; (*c*) sensory deceptions associated with affective states (anxiety, delusions of reference); (*d*) hallucinosis phantastica (paraphrenia). He questions the sensory basis of many so-called sensory deceptions.

It is apparent from a study of the literature that ever-renewed efforts have been made to evolve criteria suitable for describing and classifying the whole range of hallucinatory phenomena. The literature has grown to such proportions that Mourgue (57), for instance, found it necessary to consult more than 7000 titles. In an attempt to cope with the wealth of subjective phenomena arising under normal and pathological conditions, investigators have considered such factors as levels of reality, states of consciousness (degree of "clouding"), phenomenal appearance, the relation to "inner" and "outer" space, and the relation to "intentions" or "acts" of the subject. The employment of such criteria has led to a classification of the phenomena into hallucinations, pseudohallucinations, illusions, eidetic images, eidetic images with *Realitätscharakter,* hypnagogic images, reperceptions, *Sinnengedächtnis,* memory-after-images, pseudo-memory-images, and phantastic visual phenomena. This does not exhaust the number of distinctions drawn on various grounds. For example, hallucinations have been divided into "psychogenic" and "nonpsychogenic," *eigentliche* and *uneigentliche,* positive and negative hallucinations.

In view of the large number of distinctions available, we should expect that an investigator would have no difficulty in assigning the various sensory deceptions in his subjects or other forms of subjective experiences their proper place in a classification of hallucinatory and related phenomena. However, this is far from being the case. The *first* difficulty arises from the fact that in actual experience there are many transitions and transformations, so that, for example, an illusion or a hypnagogic image may turn into a hallucination. A *second* difficulty is more serious. It frequently happens that the hallucinatory experience of the subject is such that it cannot be adequately described and classified in terms of available concepts. Klein (30), for instance, found that current definitions were of no use in characterizing the hemianopic hallucinations of his patients and that these could be described only as "special forms of pathological experience." Many other phenomena arising under normal and pathological conditions display the same resistance to being labeled and do not fit into any classificatory scheme. In the case of eidetic imagery, for instance, the question has been raised whether the experience of the subject should be classified as a projected memory-image, a pseudohallucination, or a hallucination (28, 60). A similar question arises with regard to "mescaline hallucinations."

We have used the term "mescaline hallucinations" only to characterize the phenomena in a preliminary way. Even the self-observations of qualified observers have not settled the point whether the phenomena arising at certain stages of the poisoning should be designated as hallucinations or pseudohallucinations. Some observers hold that they are pseudohallucinations in the sense of Kandinsky; others believe that the phenomena can be described only by reference to a new concept of "pseudohallucination" different from that of Kandinsky. Instead of classifying the phenomena, some investigators have been content with references to the state of consciousness of the subject or the level of reality on which the phenomena appear. Claude and Ey (7) state that a "hallucinogenic substance" such as mescaline produces an *osmose du réel et de l'imaginaire*. Ewald (14) thinks that we are dealing with hallucinatory-dreamlike experiences occurring in "a kind of delirium without clouding of consciousness" and reports that a similarly "rich optically delirious picture" without clouding of consciousness is sometimes found in cases of chronic encephalitis and in patients with hypophysial tumors.

The fact that present concepts in the field of hallucinations cannot do justice to the wealth of normal and pathological experiences can be remedied in only two ways. It must be recognized, first, that most categories employed in describing psychic phenomena in general are neither clearly defined nor generally agreed upon. It follows that any improvement in the conceptual tools of psychology will benefit the study of hallucinations. In the second place, many normal and pathological experiences have either not been analyzed so far by using techniques already available or could not be analyzed because of the difficulties of an experimental approach. It follows that new approaches and more thorough analyses will help define more clearly the varieties of hallucinatory experiences.

Psychiatrists have recognized that many hallucinations of dementia praecox patients are not really hallucinations but, to use the German expression, *uneigentliche Halluzinationen*. Although the patients refer to sensory experiences of all kinds, it remains frequently obscure in what sense field the hallucinations occur. In fact, it is questionable whether the hallucinations really represent visual, auditory, or cenesthetic experiences or have any sensory content. It is of interest that an investigation of synesthesias in normal individuals leads into similar difficulties (27). It is true that an auditory stimulus may give rise to a sensation of color in some subjects, but in others the color, e.g., purple, is not actually *seen*. Instead, the subject experiences a "feeling like purple" or a feeling "as if purple." In these subjects it is a similarity in affective relations that is apparently responsible for the quasi-visual "as if" character of the synesthetic experience. In still another group of subjects, the auditory stimulus calls forth merely the visual image of a color.

There are also "complex synesthesias" that are characterized by the fact that the thinking of an abstract concept (infinity, peace, sin, negation, etc.) invariably leads to seeing or imagining certain colors, figures, or lines or to some "as if" experience of such colors, etc. The subject, for example, may have the experience of a "horizontal, sharp, thin, square plate of white metal" when thinking about "negation." We may say, therefore, that there are not only *eigentliche* and *uneigentliche* hallucinations but also *eigentliche* and *uneigentliche* forms of synesthesia. The results of a chemical approach to these problems, however, should warn us that we cannot entirely dismiss the possibility that certain or even all "cenesthetic hallucinations" of dementia praecox patients may have some sensory basis. The profound effects of mescaline on the sensorium are known, and yet, as Mayer-Gross (51) correctly observes, the descriptions of abnormal somatosensory experiences by mescalinized persons are often as fantastic and unintelligible as those of schizophrenics.

The *third* difficulty in arriving at clear concepts in the field of hallucinations arises from the complexity and inconstancy of "hallucination" as a symptom in a group of other symptoms. It is characteristic of drugs, disease processes, and other hallucinogenic factors and conditions that they produce more than one type of sensory deception. In fact, in some psychoses, there are apparently hallucinations of different types and of different sensory origin, "reflex hallucinations," pseudohallucinations, illusions, and almost every kind of sensory deception ever described. Bleuler has presented a truly impressive picture of the varieties of sensory deceptions in schizophrenia. Even in mescaline poisoning, we find different kinds of illusions, pseudohallucinations, and hallucinations. Furthermore, all these phenomena may be very inconstant in the sense that all or some of them may be present or absent under certain conditions or at certain stages of the disease or the poisoning. "Voices" not heard for many months may suddenly be heard again. At one time, the hallucinating may be interrupted by weak forms of external stimulation; at other times even strong stimuli are ineffective.

The fact that the same dose of mescaline may produce at different times different types of hallucinations in the same subject has led Franke (17) to suggest serial poisonings, with intervals of days instead of months. He believes that long intervals may introduce differences in the "actual biological condition" of the individual, a condition that is undoubtedly influenced by factors such as age, hunger, thirst, fatigue, weather, nutrition, emotional states, etc. The question may be raised, however, as to why certain psychic functions remain fairly constant and are only little affected by marked changes in the "actual biological condition," whereas hallucinatory phenomena and the hallucinatory process undergo marked fluctuations. It is of interest in this connection that similar fluctuations seem to be characteristic of the performances of patients with visual agnosia. For example, the patient may be able to recognize certain details or general relations on one day but not on the next, or only under certain conditions; he may be able to do it spontaneously but not at will, or vice versa. At any rate, the factors responsible for these fluctuations in hallucinatory symptoms cannot be clearly defined at present.

Mourgue (57) has advanced the view that they are due to a dysregulation of the normal relations between the vegetative system (in the sense of Kraus) and the cortex. The hallucination, according to his view, represents an invasion of the world of "instincts" into the "sphere of orientation and causality"; it is not a "morphological" but a "secretory" disorder (in the sense of Mourgue and von Monakow) indicative of disturbances in the normal relations between the "vegetative" or "instinctive" sphere and the cortex. Mourgue is not surprised that fluctuations and oscillations in hallucinatory symptoms represent the normal state of affairs, since the hallucination is essentially not a static phenomenon but a dynamic process, the instability of which merely reflects an instability in the conditions of its origin. Although the value of such concepts as "sphere of orientation and causality" and "sphere of instincts" for actual research may be questioned, there is no doubt about the importance of vegetative mechanisms for hunger, thirst, sex, sleep, and affective states. Furthermore, it appears that further information on factors influencing the excitability of the vegetative system (electrolytes and lipoids, hormones, colloidal balance, etc.) will be of far-reaching significance for the problem of hallucinations.

Research in the field of hallucinations has been dominated by two chief interests. Either the investigators have been interested in the structure of the various phenomena commonly classified as "hallucinations" or they have studied the hallucination as a "symptom" in an aggregate of other symptoms. For investigative work, it matters little whether we start from the phenomenology of hallucinatory experiences or from "syndromes with hallucinatory elements," since any thorough analysis will lead to a study of many related factors.

The hallucinatory constants that we have described are characteristic not only of certain aspects of hallucinations but also of a variety of other phenomena. The existence of these constants suggests some constancy in the underlying conditions. Other aspects of hallucinations and the hallucinatory process itself are often characterized by instability and fluctuations, and it is the task of future research to deduce the occurrence of these fluctuations from the nature of the underlying mechanisms. No one would have thought a short time ago, Mourgue points out, that there ever could be any connection between tetany and the subject of hallucinations. And, we may add, no one would have thought of electrolytes and hormones in connection with hallucinations. Ultimately we are not interested in hallucinatory constants per se but in the conditions producing them. There is no doubt that the study of these conditions will be significant for the analysis of certain disease processes and the exploration of fundamental reaction systems in normal individuals.

The phenomenological approach finally leads to the study of certain syndromes and general reaction systems in the organism; the study of "syndromes with hallucinatory elements" finally leads to an analysis of the hallucinatory phenomena. Only by studying the whole complex of symptoms in mescaline intoxication, including the hallucinatory symptoms, has it become possible to recognize mescaline as an agent for the production of "experimental psychoses," and only in such a way have psychiatrists recognized the symptomatological similarity between mescaline intoxication and the acute phases of schizophrenia (3, 4, 7, 8, 22, 47, 76). No matter what the symptomatological relations may be, the "mescal psychosis" is produced by a well-defined chemical substance and not by hypothetically assumed toxins, "metatoxic intermediaries," and the like. It seems that psychotic symptoms resembling those of mescaline intoxication appear not only in the course of the schizophrenic disease process but also under other conditions. Serko (73), for instance, described the "unusually interesting psychosis" of a patient whose symptoms were strikingly similar to those produced by mescaline. In view of these findings, it is unfortunate that at present so little is known about the biochemical processes involved in mescaline action.

To complete the picture of the total effects produced by mescaline, we should mention some facts that have a more particular bearing on the study of normal and abnormal personality. It was found, for example, that posthypnotic suggestions may influence mescaline-produced hallucinations and that, in turn, posthypnotic sensory deceptions may become altered under the influence of the drug (59). A patient with spontaneous hemianopic hallucinations declared herself *blind* for the duration of the mescalinized state (1). A patient who had not heard "voices" for half a year heard them again while under the influence of mescaline (89). Other investigators have used mescaline for more frontal attacks on problems of personality. They have been interested, for example, in the reactions of different personality types, different races, and mentally subnormal individuals and in the possibility of obtaining "confessions" during the intoxication (2, 4, 39, 47, 48, 59). The results suggest that mescaline investigations cannot be considered the royal road to "the hinterland of character" and that the chief value of this drug lies in its effectiveness as a research tool in the solution of some fundamental problems of biological psychology and psychiatry.

REFERENCES

1   Adler, A., & Pötzl, O. Über eine eigenartige Reaktion auf Meskalin bei einer Kranken mit doppelseitigen Herden in der Sehsphäre. *Jahrb. Psychiat. & Neurol.*, 1936, **53**, 13–34.

2   Bensheim, H. Typenunterschiede bei Meskalinversuchen. *Z. ges. Neurol. Psychiat.*, 1929, **121**, 531–43.

3   Beringer, K. Experimentelle Psychosen durch Mescalin. *Z. ges. Neurol. Psychiat.*, 1923, **84**, 426–33.

4   Beringer, K. Der Meskalinrausch. *Monogr. Gesamtgeb. Neurol. & Psychiat.*, 1927, **49**, 1–315.

5   Berze, J. Eigenartige Gesichtshalluzinationen in einem Falle von akuter Trinkerpsychose. *Z. ges. Neurol. Psychiat.*, 1923, **84**, 487–521.

6   Ceroni, L. L'intossicazione mescalinica. (Autoesperienze.) *Riv. sper. Freniat.*, 1932, **56**, 42–104.

7   Claude, H., & Ey, H. La mescaline, substance hallucinogène. *C. R. Soc. Biol., Paris*, 1934, **115**, 838–41.

8   Deschamps, A. Éther, cocaïne, hachich, peyotl et démence précoce. Paris: Éditions Véga, 1932, pp. 210.

9   Dybowski, M. Conditions for the appearance of hypnagogic visions. *Kwart. psychol.*, 1939, **11**, 68–94.

10 Ebbecke, U. Receptorenapparat und entoptische Erscheinungen. *Handb. norm u. pathol. Physiol.* Berlin: Springer, 1929. Vol. XII, Pt. 1, 233–65.

11 Ellis, H. Mescal, a new artificial paradise. *Ann. rep. Smithsonian Instit.* 1897, 537–48.

12 Engerth, G., Hoff, H., & Pötzl, O. Zur Patho-Physiologie der hemianopischen Halluzinationen. *Z. ges. Neurol. Psychiat.*, 1935, **152**, 399–421.

13 Epstein, A. L. Somatologische Studien zur Psychiatrie. *Z. ges. Neurol. Psychiat.*, 1933, **146**, 525–47.

14   Ewald, G. Psychosen bei akuten Infektionen, bei Allgemein-
      leiden und bei Erkrankung innerer Organe. *Handb.
      Geisteskr.*, Ergänzungsband. Berlin: Springer, 1939. Pt. 1,
      pp. 205–47.

15   Fischer, O. Ein weiterer Beitrag zur Klinik und Pathogenese
      der hysterischen Dysmegalopsie. *Mschr. Psychiat. Neurol.*,
      1907, **21**, 1–19.

16   Forster, E. Selbstversuch mit Meskalin. *Z. ges. Neurol.
      Psychiat.*, 1930, **127**, 1–14.

17   Franke, G. Variierte Serienversuche mit Meskalin. *Z. ges.
      Neurol. Psychiat.*, 1934, **150**, 427–33.

18   Gurewitsch, M. Über das interparietale Syndrom bei Gei-
      steskrankheiten. *Z. ges. Neurol. Psychiat.*, 1932, **140**, 593–
      603.

19   Gurewitsch, M. Weitere Beiträge zur Lehre vom interparie-
      talen Syndrom bei Geisteskrankheiten. *Z. ges. Neurol.
      Psychiat.*, 1933, **146**, 126–44.

20   Guttmann, A. Medikamentöse Spaltung der Persönlichkeit.
      Mschr. Psychiat. Neurol., 1924, **56**, 161–87.

21   Guttmann, E. Artificial psychoses produced by mescaline. *J.
      ment. Sci.*, 1936, **82**, 203–21.

22   Guttmann, E., & Maclay, W. S. Mescalin and depersonaliza-
      tion. *J. Neurol. Psychopath.*, 1936, **16**, 193–212.

23   Haack, K. Experimental-deskriptive Psychologie der Bewe-
      gungen, Konfigurationen und Farben unter Verwendung
      des Flimmerphaenomens. Berlin: Karger, 1927, pp. 263.

24   Hoff, H., & Pötzl, O. Über Störungen des Tiefensehens bei
      zerebraler Metamorphopsie. *Mschr. Psychiat. Neurol.*,
      1935, **90**, 305–26.

25   Hoff, H., & Pötzl, O. Zur diagnostischen Bedeutung der
      Polyopie bei Tumoren des Occipitalhirnes. *Z. ges. Neurol.
      Psychiat.*, 1935, **152**, 433–50.

26   Hoppe, I. Der entoptische Inhalt des Auges und das entop-
      tische Sehfeld beim hallucinatorischen Sehen. *Allg. Z.
      Psychiat.*, 1887, **43**, 438–52.

27   Jaensch, E. R., *et al.* Grundformen menschlichen Seins. Ber-
      lin: Elsner, 1929. Pp. xv + 524.

28   Jankowska, H. Eidetische Bilder und Halluzinationen. *Kwart.
      psychol.*, 1939, **11**, 189–230.

29   Kanner, L., & Schilder, P. Movements in optic images and the
      optic imagination of movements. *J. nerv. ment. Dis.*, 1930,
      72, 489–517.

30   Klein, R. Beitrag zur Frage der hemianopischen Halluzina-
      tionen. *Mschr. Psychiat. Neurol.*, 1936, **92**, 131–49.

31 Klien, H. Entoptische Wahrnehmung des retinalen Pigment-epithels im Migräneanfall? Z ges. Neurol. Psychiat., 1917, **36**, 323–34.

32 Klüver, H. Mescal visions and eidetic vision. Amer. J. Psychol., 1926, **37**, 502–15.

33 Klüver, H. Mescal. London: Kegan Paul, 1928. Pp. 111.

34 Klüver, H. Fragmentary eidetic imagery. Psychol. Rev., 1930, **37**, 441–58.

35 Klüver, H. Eidetic phenomena. Psychol. Bull., 1932, **29**, 181–203.

36 Klüver, H. The eidetic type. Proc. Ass. Res. nerv. & ment. Dis., 1933, **14**, 150–68.

37 Klüver, H. The study of personality and the method of equivalent and non-equivalent stimuli. Character & Pers., 1936, **5**, 91–112.

38 König, A. Eine bisher noch nicht bekannte subjective Gesichtserscheinung. Arch. Ophthal., 1884, **30**, 329–330.

39 La Barre, W. The peyote cult. New Haven: Yale Univ. Press, 1938. Pp. 188.

40 Ladd-Franklin, C. Visible radiation from excited nerve fiber: the reddish blue arcs and the reddish blue glow of the retina. Science, 1927, **66**, 239–241.

41 Lindemann, E. The neurophysiological effect of intoxicating drugs. Amer. J. Psychiat., 1934, **13**, 1007–37.

42 Lindemann, E., and Malamud, W. Experimental analysis of the psychopathological effects of intoxicating drugs. Amer. J. Psychiat., 1934, **13**, 853–79.

43 Ludlow, F. The hasheesh eater. New York: Rains, 1903. Pp. 371.

44 Maclay, W. S., & Guttmann, E. Mescaline hallucinations in artists. Arch. Neurol. Psychiat., Chicago, 1941, **45**, 130–37.

45 Maclay, W. S., Guttmann, E., & Mayer-Gross, W. Spontaneous drawings as an approach to some problems of psychopathology. Proc. roy. Soc. Med., 1938, **31**, 1337–50.

46 Maloney, W. J. M. A. Locomotor ataxia (tabes dorsalis). New York, London: Appleton, 1918. Pp. 299.

47 Marinesco, G. Recherches sur l'action de la mescaline. Presse méd., 1933, **41**, 1433–37.

48 Marinesco, M. G. Visions colorées produites par la mescaline. Presse méd., 1933, **41**, 1864–66.

49 Marshall, C. R. Entoptic phenomena associated with the retina. Brit. J. Ophthal., 1935, **19**, 177–201.

50 Marshall, C. R. An enquiry into the causes of mescal visions. *J. Neurol. Psychopath.*, 1937, **17**, 289–304.

51 Mayer-Gross, W. Psychopathologie und Klinik der Trugwahrnehmungen. *Handb. Geisteskr.*, ed. by Bumke. Berlin: Springer, 1928. Vol. I, Pt. I, pp. 427–507.

52 Mayer-Gross, W., & Stein, H. Über einige Abänderungen der Sinnestätigkeit im Meskalinrausch. *Z. ges. Neurol. Psychiat.*, 1926, **101**, 354–86.

53 Menninger-Lerchenthal, E. Das Truggebilde der eigenen Gestalt. *Abh. Neur., Psychiat., Psychol. u. ihren Grenzgeb.*, 1935, **74**, pp. iv + 196.

54 Möller, A. Einige Meskalinversuche. *Acta psychiat. et neur.*, 1935, **10**, 405–42.

55 Morgenthaler, W. Über Zeichnungen von Gesichtshalluzinationen. *Z. ges. Neurol. Psychiat.*, 1919, **45**, 19–29.

56 Morselli, G. E. Contribution à la psychopathologie de l'intoxication par la mescaline. *J. de Psychol.*, 1936, **33**, 368–92.

57 Mourgue, R. Neurobiologie de l'hallucination. Bruxelles: Lamertin, 1932. Pp. 416.

58 Neuhaus, W. Makropsie und Mikropsie bei Basedowoiden. *Z. ges. Neurol. Psychiat.*, 1926, **105**, 257–313.

59 Pap, Z. v. Einwirkung des Meskalinrausches auf die posthypnotischen Sinnestäuschungen. *Z. ges. Neurol. Psychiat.*, 1936, **155**, 655–64.

60 Pisk, G. Zur Frage der Pseudohalluzinationen bei der Schizophrenie und ihrer Beziehungen zur eidetischen Anlage. *Mschr. Psychiat. Neurol.*, 1936, **92**, 150–56.

61 Pötzl, O. Tachystoskopisch provozierte optische Halluzinationen bei einem Falle von Alkoholhalluzinose mit rückgebildeter zerebraler Hemianopsie. *Jahrb. Psychiat. Neurol.*, 1915, **35**, 141–46.

62 Pötzl, O. Experimentell erregte Traumbilder in ihren Beziehungen zum indirekten Sehen. *Z. ges. Neurol. Psychiat.*, 1917, **37**, 278–349.

63 Pötzl, O., & Urban, H. Über die isoliert erhaltene temporale Sichel bei zerebraler Hemianopsie. *Mschr. Psychiat. Neurol.*, 1936, **92**, 67–106.

64 Purkinje, J. E. Opera omnia. Prague: Society of Czech Physicians, 1918. Vol. I, pp. 1–162.

65 Rohracher, H. Ueber subjektive Lichterscheinungen bei Reizung mit Wechselströmen. *Z. Sinnesphysiol.*, 1935–1936, **66**, 164–81.

66 Schilder, P. Über monokuläre Polyopie bei Hysterie. *Dtsch. Z. Nervenheilk*, 1920, **66**, 250–60.

67 Schilder, P. Über Halluzinationen. *Z. ges. Neurol. Psychiat.*, 1920, **53**, 169–98.

68 Schilder, P. Psychoanalyse und Eidetik. *Z. Sex.-Wiss.*, 1926, **13**, 56–61.

69 Schilder, P. Experiments on imagination, after-images and hallucinations. *Amer. J. Psychiat.*, 1933, **13**, 597–609.

70 Schilder, P. The vestibular apparatus in neurosis and psychosis. *J. nerv. ment. Dis.*, 1933, **78**, 1–23, 137–64.

71 Schröder, P. Das Halluzinieren. *Z. ges. Neurol. Psychiat.*, 1926, **101**, 599–614.

72 Serko, A. Im Mescalinrausch. *Jahrb. Psychiat. Neurol.*, 1913, **34**, 355–66.

73 Serko, A. Über einen eigenartigen Fall von Geistesstörung. *Z. ges. Neurol. Psychiat.*, 1919, **44**, 21–78.

74 Skworzoff, K. Doppelgänger-Halluzinationen bei Kranken mit Funktionsstörungen des Labyrinths. *Z. ges. Neurol. Psychiat.*, 1931, **133**, 762–66.

75 Stein, J. Über die Veränderung der Sinnesleistungen und die Entstehung von Trugwahrnehmungen. *Handb. Geisteskr.*, ed. by Bumke. Berlin: Springer, 1928. Vol. I, Pt. I, pp. 352–426.

76 Stockings, G. T. A clinical study of the mescaline psychosis, with special reference to the mechanism of the genesis of schizophrenic and other psychotic states. *J. ment. Sci.*, 1940, **86**, 29–47.

77 Szuman, S. Analiza formalna i psychologiczna widzeń meskalinowych. *Kwart. psychol.*, 1930, **1**, 156–212. *Cf.* summary in German, pp. 214–20.

78 Urban, H. Zur Physiologie der Okzipitalregion des Menschen. *Mschr. Psychiat. Neurol.*, 1935, **92**, 32–39.

79 Urbantschitsch, V. Über subjektive optische Anschauungsbilder. Leipzig, Wien: Deuticke, 1907. Pp. vi + 211.

80 Urbantschitsch, V. Über subjektive Hörerscheinungen und subjektive optische Anschauungsbilder. Leipzig, Wien: Deuticke, 1908. Pp. iv. + 123.

81 Veit, F., & Vogt, M. Die Verteilung subcutan verabreichter Alkaloide auf verschiedene Regionen des Zentralnervensystems. *Naturwiss.*, 1934, **22**, 492–94.

82 Vogt, M. Die Verteilung von Arzneistoffen auf verschiedene Regionen des Zentralnervensystems, zugleich ein Beitrag zu ihrer quantitativen Mikrobestimmung im Gewebe. II.